CONSERVATION LAWS
— and —
CONCEPT-BASED PROBLEM SOLVING

Minds·On
PHYSICS

Activities & Reader

CONSERVATION LAWS
—— and ——
CONCEPT-BASED PROBLEM SOLVING

Minds·On PHYSICS

Activities & Reader

William J. Leonard

Robert J. Dufresne

William J. Gerace

Jose P. Mestre

The University of Massachusetts
Physics Education Research Group

KENDALL/HUNT PUBLISHING COMPANY
4050 Westmark Drive   Dubuque, Iowa 52002

Also available in the Minds•On Physics Series

Minds•On Physics: Motion / Activities & Reader

Teacher's Guide to accompany Minds•On Physics: Motion

Minds•On Physics: Interactions / Activities & Reader

Teacher's Guide to accompany Minds•On Physics: Interactions

Teacher's Guide to accompany Minds•On Physics: Conservation Laws & Concept-Based Problem Solving

Minds•On Physics: Fundamental Forces & Fields / Activities & Reader

Teacher's Guide to accompany Minds•On Physics: Fundamental Forces & Fields

Minds•On Physics: Complex Systems / Activities & Reader

Teacher's Guide to accompany Minds•On Physics: Complex Systems

Minds•On Physics: Advanced Topics in Mechanics / Activities & Reader

Teacher's Guide to accompany Minds•On Physics: Advanced Topics in Mechanics

Author Address for Correspondence

William J. Leonard
Department of Physics
Box 34525
University of Massachusetts
Amherst, MA 01003–4525 USA

e-mail: WJLEONARD@physics.umass.edu

Cover Photos: Image of roller coaster "The Dragon"
courtesy of Adventureland Park, Des Moines, Iowa.
Tennis player image © 1997 PhotoDisc.
All other images courtesy of Corel.

ISBN 0-7872-3931-3

This book was prepared with the support of NSF Grant: ESI 9255713.
However, any opinions, findings, conclusions and or recommendations herein
are those of the authors and do not necessarily reflect the views of NSF.

Printed in the United States of America
10 9 8 7 6 5 4

Contents

How to Use this Book   xiii

Acknowledgments   xv

Activities

continued

Activities (continued)

Reader
Chapter 3: Conservation Laws

Reader (continued)

continued

Reader (continued)

Reader (continued)

continued

Reader (continued)

Reader (continued)

continued

Reader (continued)

Chapter 4: Concept-Based Problem Solving

How to Use this Book

The activities in this book are designed to get you *thinking about* and *doing* physics — in a way that is a lot closer to the way professional scientists think about and do science. You will learn by communicating your ideas with your teacher and with other students, and by trying to make sense of the ideas presented in the book.

During the school year, you may be required to memorize some definitions, vocabulary, and other basic information, but you should <u>not</u> try to memorize the answers to specific questions and problems. Answer should *make sense to you*. If they do not make sense to you, then you probably should go back and change how you think about the problem or situation. Even if everyone else seems to understand something, please do not give up! Keep trying until it makes sense to you.

We want *everyone* in the class to understand physics, and we sincerely believe that everyone *can* learn to understand physics, because the activities are intended to help everyone develop the skills needed to learn physics. If necessary, your teacher and your classmates should be able to help you. Find out how they think about a problem or situation, and adapt their ideas to your own way of thinking. And if you are helping someone else, remember that everyone learns at a different rate, so please be patient.

This style of learning requires a lot of dedication and work, especially if you are not familiar with the style. In the short run, this style might seem impossible and not worth the extra effort. But in the long run, it is definitely worth it. We really, really want you to memorize *as little as possible*. Focus on the ideas that are most widely useful, and learn how to use these to derive the relationships you might need to answer a question or solve a problem. You will be able to solve lots of problems using this approach, and you will develop skills that will be useful in any field you might choose to enter. Remember that physics is one way — among many — of looking at the natural world. It's a way of analyzing, evaluating, describing, explaining and predicting the behavior of objects and collections of objects.

Acknowledgments

The *concept-based problem-solving* approach to learning is the way Bill Gerace has taught hundreds of graduate and undergraduate students at the University of Massachusetts. It is his approach that has been refined, modified, and adapted to create the activities in this book.

We are deeply grateful to the National Science Foundation for funding the pilot project, *Materials for Developing Concept-Based Problem-Solving Skills in Physics*, under grant MDR–9050213. Although we had no prior experience writing materials for high-school physics, the Foundation reasoned that as experts in both physics and cognitive research, we were uniquely qualified to bring a fresh outlook to the task. We thank NSF also for funding the renewal, *Minds-On Physics: An Integrated Curriculum for Developing Concept-Based Problem Solving in Physics*, under grant ESI–9255713. The materials in this book are a direct result of this funding and are also evidence of how federal support can impact education and stimulate reform. We thank Gerhard Salinger, our project director at NSF, for his unwavering support of our approach and his many suggestions.

We are very fortunate to have found four wonderful teachers who were willing to try a different approach to teaching physics by field-testing those first 24 "modules" of the pilot project: Charlie Camp (Amherst Regional HS, Amherst, MA), Mike Cunha (Weaver HS, Hartford, CT), Steve Degon (Central HS, Springfield, MA) and Hughes Pack (Northfield–Mount Hermon School, Northfield, MA). They let us into their classrooms and let us see first-hand how their students dealt with the approach. Their numerous suggestions have improved the materials and the approach greatly.

We also thank all the teachers who have field-tested the Minds•On Physics activities: Jane Barrett (Howard School of Academics & Technology, Chattanooga, TN), Larry Blanchard (Warren Easton HS, New Orleans, LA), Roger Blough (Tyner HS, Chattanooga, TN), Gaby Blum (Monument Mountain Regional HS, Great Barrington, MA), Charlie Camp (ARHS), Jim Carter (Saugus HS, Saugus, MA), Jack Czajkowski (Pioneer Valley Regional School District, MA), John Dark (Brainerd HS, Chattanooga, TN), Steve Degon (Central HS), Ed Eckel (NMH), Jen DuBois (NMH), Jake Foster (Hixson HS, Hixson, TN), Bill Fraser (Chattanooga Phoenix School 3, Chattanooga, TN), Ken Gano (Hixson HS), Dennis Gilbert (Taconic HS, Pittsfield, MA), Craig Hefner (NMH), Ray Janke (Chicopee HS, Chicopee, MA), Aaron Kropf (ARHS), Bernie Lally (Chicopee HS), Michael Oliphant (Millis HS, Millis, MA), Hughes Pack (NMH), Jerry

Pate (Chattanooga School for Arts and Sciences, Chattanooga, TN), Kirk Rau (Tyner HS), Jessie Royal (Dade County HS, Trenton, GA), Cheryl Ryan (Hoosac Valley Regional HS, Adams, MA), John Safko (The University of South Carolina), Glenda Schmidt (Slidell HS, Slidell, LA), Lisa Schmitt (NMH), Steve Schultheis (Saugus HS), Lance Simpson (NMH), Mark Walcroft (Taconic HS), Mark Wenig (CSAS), Maxine Willis (Gettysburg HS, Gettysburg, PA), Melany O'Connor (NMH), and Tom Winn (McMain HS, New Orleans, LA). They often had little warning about what and when materials would arrive, and usually had just a few days to prepare themselves to do the activities in class. We appreciate their patience and understanding. We also thank them for recommending that we create extensive teacher support materials. Although this addition has nearly doubled the scope of the project, it is a welcome change, and every teacher who uses the Minds•On Physics materials is indebted to them.

We thank Kris Chapman and Maggie Coffin for many of the drawings used in the activities. They brought a style and grace to the figures that none of us could ever match. We thank Ian Beatty for creating the Town of King's Court. We also thank Gary Bradway (Berkshire Community College, Pittsfield, MA), for his frequent help with conceptualizing and revising the early activities; Jerry Touger (Curry College, Milton, MA), for his help writing the Reader; and George Collison (The Concord Consortium, Concord, MA), for showing us how hands-on activities may be combined with minds-on activities.

Thanks to Allan Feldman (University of Massachusetts, Amherst, MA) and the rest of his evaluation team (Karla, Jim, Ed, Sonal, and Aaron) for evaluating the materials and its implementation.

We are thankful to Kendall/Hunt for publishing these materials. We are particularly thankful to the people at K/H for their many ideas and suggestions, especially regarding the format and style of these materials.

Special thanks also to all our friends and relatives.

Bill Leonard
Bob Dufresne
Bill Gerace
Jose Mestre

The UMass Physics Education Research Group
Department of Physics & Astronomy
Box 34525
University of Massachusetts
Amherst, MA 01003-4525 USA

Visit us on the Web at http://www-perg.phast.umass.edu/

Activities

71–95:
CONSERVATION LAWS

— & —

96–102:
CONCEPT-BASED PROBLEM SOLVING

71

Investigating Collisions in which Two Objects Stick Together

Purpose and Expected Outcome

To prepare yourself for learning about *momentum*, you must first learn how the masses and velocities of two objects affect the outcome of their interaction. In this activity, you will study collisions between two carts that stick to one another and move together afterwards. You will see that there is a definite pattern to the final velocity of the combination, which depends on the circumstances just prior to each collision.

Prior Experience / Knowledge Needed

You should be familiar with the concepts of mass, weight, velocity, speed, acceleration, and force. You should be able to weigh objects and to estimate the speed of moving objects.

Explanation of Activity

In this activity, two objects collide and stick together. In each case, object A is moving, and object B is at rest just before the collision. You will consider different masses for each of the objects, and different speeds for object A.

To do this activity, you will need:

- **Two dynamics carts** (or their equivalent, as long as the friction in the wheel-bearings is very small). The carts must be designed so that they will stick together when they collide.

- **Modeling clay** (or some other means of changing the masses of the carts). You should have at least enough clay to double the masses of both carts at the same time.

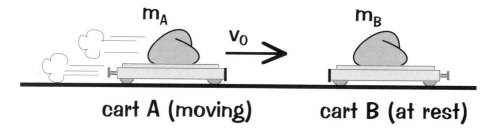

cart A (moving)   cart B (at rest)

After each collision, the two carts should stick together and move with (the same) constant velocity. Usually this means that the carts should be lined up, perhaps on a track, so that they move together easily after becoming attached.

A1. **Determining the effect of the mass of the moving cart on the final velocity.**
Practice launching the cart in a consistent manner. The objective is to have cart A always have the same velocity just before the collision occurs. (Perhaps you can devise some way to cause the speed to be the same each time.)

(a) Use the same mass for both carts. How does the final velocity compare to the initial velocity? (Consider both speed and direction of motion.) Make the best estimates you can of the velocities.

(b) Vary the mass of the moving cart (A), and note how the final velocity changes. (Remember to keep the initial velocity as consistent as possible.) Again, estimate the velocities as best you can.

(c) Describe how the final velocity depends on the mass of the moving cart. For instance, make a sketch of final velocity versus mass of the moving cart (A).

continued

A2. Determining the effect of the mass of the stationary cart on the final velocity. As in A1, use the same initial velocity for cart A each time you make the carts collide. Repeat each set of circumstances as needed to make sure of your results.

(a) Vary the mass of the <u>stationary</u> cart, and note how the final velocity changes. As before, remember to keep the initial velocity as consistent as possible, and make your estimates as well as you can.

(b) Describe how the final velocity depends on the mass of the stationary cart. Sketch the final velocity versus the mass of the stationary cart (B).

A3. Determining the effect of the initial velocity of the moving cart on the final velocity. Throughout this step, keep the masses of the carts the same, as in part (a) of both A1 and A2.

(a) Vary the velocity of the moving cart and note how the final velocity changes. Make your estimates of the final velocity as well as you can.

(b) Describe how the final velocity depends on the initial velocity of the moving cart. Make a sketch to represent this relationship.

Reflection

When describing (or sketching) how the final velocity (v_f) depends upon other quantities (m_A, m_B, and v_0), it is useful to consider *limiting cases*. In this reflection, you will use limiting cases to deepen your understanding of the phenomena you have just finished studying.

R1. (a) What would you predict would happen if the stationary mass (m_B) became very, very large compared to the moving mass (m_A)? What would occur if m_B were made very small?

(b) For each of the other variables (m_A and v_0) predict what would happen to v_f if each became very small (tended toward zero) and very large (tended toward infinity).

R2. Which of your sketches from the activity look like straight lines? Which should probably <u>not</u> be straight lines? Why not? (I.e., explain why they should be curved lines.)

R3. Using all of the trends observed during this activity, can you deduce a single expression for the final velocity of the combined carts (v_f) in terms of the given variables (m_A, m_B, and v_0)? What does your expression predict will happen if both masses are very, very large but equal to each other? Does your expression work when one mass is very large and the other is very small? Explain.

72

Introducing the Concepts of Impulse and Momentum

Purpose and Expected Outcome

You already know how to solve problems in which objects undergo constant acceleration. In this activity, you will solve a few of these problems and learn that there is a close relationship between the vector quantities $\mathbf{F}_{net} \times \Delta t$ and $m \times \mathbf{v}$. These two new quantities are called *impulse* and *momentum*. In a later activity, you will learn how to define impulse when the net force is not constant.

Prior Experience / Knowledge Needed

You should be familiar with kinematics, vectors, forces, free-body diagrams, and Newton's laws. Also, you should have some experience solving both kinematics and dynamics problems.

Explanation of Activity

In this activity, you will solve three problems in which the acceleration of the central object is constant. The results will then be used to complete the Reflection. The purpose of solving these problems is to help you recognize patterns among kinematic and dynamic quantities, such as mass, velocity, net force, and time. Therefore, please take great care in getting the answers to these problems 100% correct, so that the Reflection can be completed successfully.

Use $g = 10$N/kg throughout. Ignore buoyancy and air resistance.

A1. A 0.140kg baseball is thrown <u>straight up</u> into the air with an initial speed of 15m/s.

   (a) What is the velocity of the baseball after 2 seconds?

   (b) What is the <u>change</u> in velocity after 2 seconds?

A2. A crate weighing 100N slides across a rough horizontal surface having $\mu_k = 0.12$. The initial speed of the crate is $v_0 = 4$m/s. How long does it take for the crate to slide to a stop?

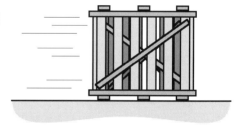

A3. Immediately after being kicked, a 0.40kg soccer ball has a speed of 30m/s and is directed at an angle of 60° above the horizontal. (See diagram.) Written as components ...

   (a) ... what is the ball's initial velocity (just after being kicked), and

   (b) ... what is the ball's velocity after 1 second?

Reflection

R1. Now that you have solved these three problems, you can look for relationships between various physical quantities. For each of the processes, <u>during the given time interval after being released</u>, make a table showing each of the following quantities. (Some values have been filled in.) Use the arrows ←, ↓, etc. to indicate the direction of vector quantities.

(a) $\mathbf{F}_{net}$ the net force;

(b) Δt the length of the specified time interval;

(c) m the mass of the object;

(d) $\mathbf{v}_0$ the initial velocity (i.e., at the beginning of the specified time interval);

(e) $\mathbf{v}_f$ the final velocity (i.e., at the end of the specified time interval); — and —

(f) $\Delta \mathbf{v}$ the change in velocity during the time interval.

Then, using the information in columns (a) through (f) ...

(g) ... compute the product $\mathbf{F}_{net} \times \Delta t$;

(h) ... compute the product $m \times \Delta \mathbf{v}$; — and —

(i) ... compare these two products to each other. Note that $\mathbf{F}_{net} \times \Delta t$ and $m \times \Delta \mathbf{v}$ are vector quantities and must have their directions indicated.

Process	$\mathbf{F}_{net}$ (N)	Δt (s)	m (kg)	$\mathbf{v}_0$ (m/s)	$\mathbf{v}_f$ (m/s)	$\Delta \mathbf{v}$ (m/s)	$\mathbf{F}_{net}\Delta t$ (N-s)	$m\Delta \mathbf{v}$ (kg-m/s)	The same or different?
A1. Ball is thrown straight up	2	0.14					2.8 ↓		SAME / DIFFERENT
A2. Crate slides to a stop						4 ←		40 ←	SAME / DIFFERENT
A3. Ball is kicked into the air	1	0.4		15→, 26↑					SAME / DIFFERENT

R2. In how many of the processes above is the quantity $\mathbf{F}_{net}\Delta t$ equal to $m\Delta \mathbf{v}$?

R3. In process A3, what is the horizontal component of $\mathbf{F}_{net}\Delta t$? What is the horizontal component of $m\Delta \mathbf{v}$? Are they equal to each other? What can you say about the direction of $\mathbf{F}_{net}\Delta t$ as compared to the direction of $m\Delta \mathbf{v}$? Explain.

R4. What are the units of $\mathbf{F}_{net}\Delta t$? What are the units of $m\Delta \mathbf{v}$? Show that these two units are equal to each other.

R5. For each of the processes above, compute $m\mathbf{v}_0$, $m\mathbf{v}_f$, and $\Delta(m\mathbf{v})$. Is the quantity $\Delta(m\mathbf{v})$ equal to the quantity $m\Delta \mathbf{v}$ in all cases? Explain. Under what conditions (if any) might they be different from each other?

Summary

We have shown that if the net force exerted on an object is constant, then $\mathbf{F}_{net}\Delta t$ (called the *impulse*) is equal to the <u>change</u> in $m\mathbf{v}$ (the *momentum*). Mathematically,

$$\mathbf{F}_{net}\,\Delta t = \Delta(m\mathbf{v}) \qquad \text{(for constant net force)}$$

This is a *vector* equation, meaning that the magnitude of the impulse is equal to the magnitude of the change in momentum, and the direction of the impulse is equal to the direction of the change in momentum. We can also say that each component of the impulse is equal to the corresponding component of the change in momentum.

In the following activities, we will provide a more general definition of impulse, and show how the concepts of impulse and momentum can be used to analyze physical situations and solve problems.

73

Using Impulse and Momentum to Solve Constant-Force Problems

Purpose and Expected Outcome

The concepts of impulse and momentum can help you solve problems efficiently, especially when the problems are too complex to use Newton's laws. In this activity, you will solve several problems two different ways: (1) using kinematics and/or dynamics, and (2) using impulse and momentum. You will then compare the efficiency of the two approaches. Finally, you will consider additional problems, deciding which approach is preferred and then using it to solve the problem.

Prior Experience / Knowledge Needed

You should be familiar with kinematics, vectors, forces, free-body diagrams, and Newton's laws. Also, you should have some experience solving both kinematics and dynamics problems.

IMPULSE AND MOMENTUM

For an object experiencing a constant acceleration during a particular time interval, the product $\mathbf{F}_{net}\Delta t$ is always equal to the <u>change</u> in the product $m\mathbf{v}$. We define the *impulse* $\mathbf{J}$ delivered by a constant force $\mathbf{F}$ during a time interval as:

$$\mathbf{J} \equiv \mathbf{F} \times \Delta t \qquad \text{definition of impulse for a constant force}$$

where Δt is the length of the time interval. Impulse is a vector quantity, and it has units of newton-seconds (N-s). The impulse always refers to a particular <u>process</u>, spanning a particular time interval.

continued

A related quantity is the *momentum* **p** defined as the product of an object's mass and its velocity:

$$\mathbf{p} \equiv m \times \mathbf{v}$$ **definition of momentum for a single object**

Momentum is also a vector quantity and has units of kg-m/s. The momentum always refers to a particular <u>instant of time</u>. As the velocity of an object changes (with time) so does its momentum.

Using Newton's second law, we can relate the *net impulse* $\mathbf{J}_{net}$ delivered to an object and the change in an object's momentum:

$$\mathbf{J}_{net} = \Delta\mathbf{p} = \Delta(m\mathbf{v})$$ **Impulse–Momentum Theorem**

This relationship is called the *Impulse–Momentum Theorem*. If the net force is the same throughout the time interval, we can write:

$$\mathbf{F}_{net}\,\Delta t = m\,\Delta\mathbf{v}$$ (for constant net force)

Explanation of Activity

PART A: Solving Problems Using Different Methods

Solve each problem using kinematics and/or dynamics. Then check your answer using $\mathbf{J}_{net} = \Delta\mathbf{p}$. Show <u>both</u> methods clearly on a separate piece of paper.

Use $g = 10$N/kg throughout. Ignore buoyancy and air resistance.

A1. A 0.14kg ball is thrown <u>straight up</u> into the air with an initial speed of 26m/s. <u>When</u> is the ball at its highest point?

A2. A 400g soccer ball has a speed of 30m/s and is directed at an angle of 60° above the horizontal as shown on the left. How long does it take before the ball reaches its minimum speed?

A3. A 120N crate slides across a floor having $\mu_k = 0.10$ (as shown on the right). The initial speed of the crate is $v_0 = 6$m/s. How fast is the crate moving after 2 seconds?

PART B: Deciding How You Will Determine the Unknown

For each part of each problem, first indicate in words <u>how</u> you will solve for the desired unknown. For example, will you use kinematics, or dynamics, or both kinematics and dynamics, or impulse and momentum, or a definition? Then, determine the unknown quantity using the method you have chosen.

B1. A 20g marble rolls across the floor at a constant speed of 2m/s and hits a wall. The marble rebounds off the wall with a speed of 1.8m/s going in exactly the opposite direction as before. The marble is in contact with the wall for 0.001 seconds.

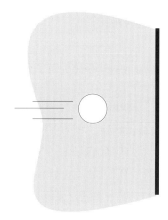

   (a) What is the change in velocity of the marble?

   (b) What is the marble's average acceleration while rebounding off the wall?

   (c) What is the average normal force exerted by the wall while the marble is in contact with it?

B2. (top view)

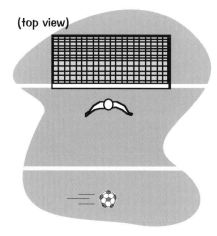

A 0.4kg soccer ball is rolling at 3m/s along a level playing field in front of the goal. A player kicks the ball with a horizontal force of 80N for 0.02s. The direction of the force is perpendicular to the direction of motion of the ball before impact.

   (a) What is the new velocity of the soccer ball?

   (b) Now suppose that we want to change the direction of the ball's motion, but not its speed, and we want the new direction to be perpendicular to the initial direction (that is, <u>directly</u> toward the goalie). What force (assuming the same time interval of 0.02s) is needed to accomplish this?

Reflection

In this Reflection, you will consider the reasons you chose one method over another to solve the preceding problems, and compare your choices with those of the rest of the class.

R1. In part A, which method yielded the correct result more often? Why do you suppose this happened? Explain.

R2. In part B, how did you decide which method to use to find the desired unknown? For example, when you chose kinematics, what feature of the problem or situation made you choose it? When you chose to use dynamics, what were the relevant features? And when you used impulse/momentum?

R3. Which seems easier for you to apply, Newton's 2nd law or impulse/momentum ideas? Discuss with your classmates.

Analyzing Collisions Using Newton's Third Law

Purpose and Expected Outcome

One of the most important reasons for studying impulse and momentum is to understand the outcomes of collisions without knowing the details of the forces exerted during them. In this activity, you will learn how Newton's third law of motion (Mathematically, $\mathbf{F}_{\text{on 1 due to 2}} = -\mathbf{F}_{\text{on 2 due to 1}}$) can be used to analyze collisions. You will also learn some of the conditions under which the *total* momentum of a system does not change.

Prior Experience / Knowledge Needed

You should be familiar with Newton's 3rd Law of Motion, with graphs of force vs. time, with the definitions of impulse and momentum, and with the Impulse–Momentum Theorem ($\mathbf{J}_{\text{net}} = \Delta\mathbf{p}$).

NEWTON'S 3RD LAW AND COLLISIONS

Whenever two objects interact, each exerts a force on the other. The magnitudes of these two forces are exactly equal, and their directions are exactly opposite, <u>instant by instant</u>. Collisions occur when two objects interact over a relatively short time period, such as when a marble hits a wall, a ball bounces off the ground, or two cars hit each other. Because Newton's 3rd law relates the forces that each object exerts on the other, we will use it to study impulses delivered by each object to the other. Then, when we understand the relationship between these two impulses, we will look at how momentum is transferred from one object to the other.

Explanation of Activity and Example

There are two parts to this activity. In the first part, you will look at the forces that two objects exert on each other. In the second part, you will look at the impulses and changes in momentum within different systems of objects.

PART A: Relating the Forces Exerted on Interacting Objects

For each of the situations below, you will be given information about some of the forces exerted. Use the given information, along with physical principles (such as Newton's laws of motion), to determine the other forces exerted.

Example. A 1kg cart rolls at 30cm/s toward another 1kg cart at rest. When they collide, the moving cart exerts the force shown below on the stationary cart. Sketch the force that the stationary cart exerts on the moving cart during the same time period.

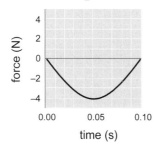

Answer: *The force exerted by the stationary cart on the moving cart is shown to the right.*

Explanation: *The forces that two objects exert on each other during any time period are always equal and opposite.*

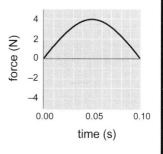

A1. A father (mass 80kg) and daughter (mass 50kg) are rollerblading. The daughter gives her father a push according to the graph shown at right.

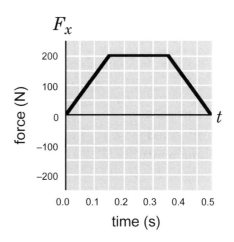

(a) Sketch the force exerted by the father on the daughter during the same time period. (Be sure to label the vertical axis.)

(b) What physical principle did you use to make your sketch?

(c) What other forces are exerted on the father and the daughter during this time period?

A2. A softball player jumps straight up into the air to catch a line drive. (The player weighs about 300 times as much as the softball.) The force exerted by the ball on the player is shown to the right.

(a) On a copy of this graph, sketch the force exerted by the player on the ball.

(b) What other forces are exerted on the player and on the ball while the ball is being caught?

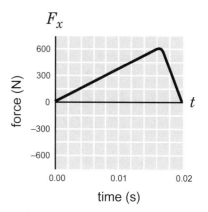

Summary

Newton's third law of motion says that whenever two objects interact, the forces that each exerts on the other are equal in magnitude and opposite in direction. This relationship is <u>independent</u> of the masses and the velocities of the two objects. The masses do, however, affect the <u>responses</u> of the objects to the interaction. So, for example, when one object is much heavier than the other, the acceleration of the heavier object will be much smaller than the acceleration of the other, and hence, the change in its velocity will be much smaller than the change in the velocity of the lighter object. If the heavier object is moving relatively quickly, then the change in its velocity might be hard to notice. This is why you might think that a bowling pin exerts no force on a bowling ball that collides with it. The velocity of the ball does not <u>appear</u> to change, while the change in velocity of the pin is very evident. In fact, the ball is slowing down very slightly. Note that the increase in momentum of the bowling pin (2.8kg-m/s, directed to the right) is opposite to the decrease in momentum of the bowling ball (2.8kg-m/s, directed to the left).

BEFORE:

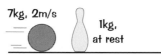

7kg, 2m/s

1kg, at rest

AFTER:

1kg, 2.8m/s

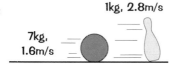

7kg, 1.6m/s

Mathematically, we write Newton's third law as:

$$\mathbf{F}_{\text{on 1 by 2}} = -\mathbf{F}_{\text{on 2 by 1}}.$$

and graphically, we can represent this relationship as shown on the right for an arbitrary interaction.

In the next part, you will use the Impulse–Momentum Theorem to determine changes in momentum.

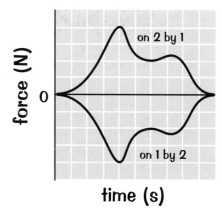

PART B: Calculating Changes in Momentum

In each of the situations described below, calculate the impulse delivered during the indicated time period by each of the forces exerted. Use $g = 10$N/kg and ignore buoyancy and air resistance throughout.

B1. A father (mass 80kg) and daughter (mass 50kg) are each at rest on rollerblades. The daughter gives her father a push according to the graph shown on the right. (You may assume that the friction force on each person is negligibly small.)

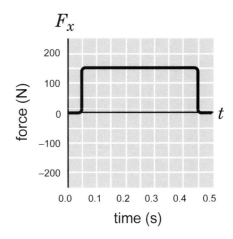

(a) What is the impulse delivered by the daughter to her father? What is the impulse delivered by the father to his daughter?

(b) What is the total impulse delivered to each of them by other forces during this time period?

(c) What are their changes in momentum during this time period?

(d) What is the total momentum of the system ($\mathbf{p}_{\text{daughter}} + \mathbf{p}_{\text{father}}$) at $t = 0$s?

(e) What is the total momentum of the system at $t = 0.5$s?

B2. A father (mass 80kg) and daughter (mass 50kg) are on rollerblades as shown in the previous problem. The daughter gives her father a push according to the graph shown to the right. (You may assume that the friction force on each person is negligibly small.)

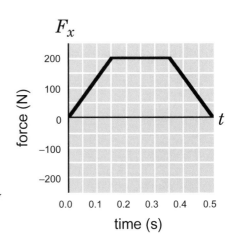

(a) This problem differs from problem B1 in that the force changes over time. How would you find the impulse delivered by the daughter in this case?

(b) Is this impulse related to the impulse delivered by the father? How are they related? Explain your reasoning.

(c) What is the total momentum of the system at $t = 0.5$s? Explain your reasoning.

continued

B3. Three ¼ kg carts are arranged as shown below. When cart B collides with cart A they stick together and move together with one-third the original velocity of B.

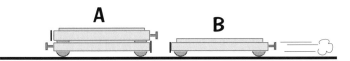

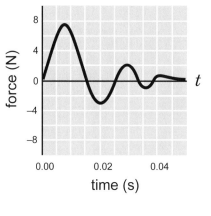

(a) Which cart, A or B, exerts the horizontal contact force shown in the graph to the right? Explain.

(b) On a separate set of axes, sketch the given force and its reaction as a function of time. Explain your reasoning.

(c) Estimate the impulse delivered to cart A by cart B. Explain.

(d) Estimate the initial speed of cart B. Explain.

Summary

Newton's 3rd law, combined with the definition of impulse and the Impulse–Momentum Theorem, allows us to identify those situations for which the total momentum within a system of objects stays the same. Mathematically, we represent this as:

$$\Delta \mathbf{P}_{system} = 0,$$

$$- \text{ or } -$$

$$\mathbf{P}_{initial} = \mathbf{P}_{final},$$

where: $\mathbf{P}_{system}$ = the total momentum of the system

= the vector sum of the individual momentums of all the objects in the system

= $\mathbf{p}_1 + \mathbf{p}_2 + \mathbf{p}_3 + \dots$,

$\mathbf{P}_{initial}$ = initial value of the total momentum, — and —

$\mathbf{P}_{final}$ = final value of the total momentum.

Momentum is conserved when there is no net external force on the system, because then there is no net impulse delivered to the system. This can happen in two ways: (1) when there are <u>no</u> external forces; and (2) when all external forces are balanced.

continued

Momentum is <u>approximately</u> conserved when the net impulse on a system is small compared to the impulses delivered to the objects in the system. This happens when the forces between objects in the system (*internal forces*) are large compared to the net force on the system (*net external force*). For example, when two carts collide, the gravitational and normal forces balance, but there is a small net force on the system due to friction. If the friction force is small enough compared to the forces exerted by the carts on each other, then momentum is approximately conserved during the collision.

Momentum is conserved in these situations because the impulse delivered to one object by a second object is equal and opposite to the impulse delivered by the second to the first. Each impulse represents a change in momentum, so the momentum given to one object must be taken away from the other. Within a system for which only internal forces are relevant, momentum is transferred between pairs of objects in the system, and the total momentum of the system remains constant.

Reflection

R1. A marble hits a wall and rebounds with the same speed it had before. Is the momentum of the marble conserved? Explain.

R2. For one of the situations in part A, there were no <u>net</u> external forces exerted on the objects. Which one? In the other one, what is the direction of the net external force on the system?

R3. Reconsider problem A2, and assume that the softball player has a mass of 60kg. The impulse delivered by the ball on the player is about 6N-s. What is the impulse delivered by the gravitational force on the player while the ball is being caught? Is this value negligible compared to the impulse delivered by the ball? Is the total momentum (of the player and ball) conserved? Explain. Which <u>component</u> of the total momentum is conserved? Explain.

Relating Momentum Ideas to One-Body Problem Situations

Purpose and Expected Outcome

In order to use momentum and impulse ideas effectively to solve problems, you must first learn how each idea relates to physical objects and to the forces exerted on those objects. In this activity, you will examine situations in which the forces on objects are known, and you will see how the magnitude and direction of each force affect each object's momentum, its *change* in momentum, and the net impulse delivered to it during a specified time period.

Prior Experience / Knowledge Needed

You should know the common forces, and know how each changes with circumstance. You should know the definitions of momentum and impulse. You should know that momentum refers to a particular instant of time, while impulse and *change* in momentum refer to a process extending over a definite period of time. You should have some experience with the Impulse–Momentum Theorem.

Explanation of Activity and Example

For <u>each</u> of the situations described below, answer the following questions for the specified time interval.

(a) List all of the forces exerted on the object. Describe any changes in the net force during the time interval.

(b) Does the object have an initial momentum? Describe any changes in its momentum.

(c) Does the object experience a net impulse?

Example. A sled accelerates from rest down an icy slope. Ignore the effects of friction and air resistance.

Answers:

(a) *The forces exerted on the sled are a gravitational force due to the earth and a normal force due to the slope. The net force does not change as the sled travels down the slope.*

(b) *The sled is initially at rest, so it has no momentum. Its momentum increases with time.*

(c) *Yes, there is a net impulse on the sled.*

A1. A large boulder sits at rest on the side of a small hill.

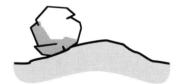

A2. A crate sits inside a railroad car, which is moving with constant speed on a straight, level track. (Consider only the crate.)

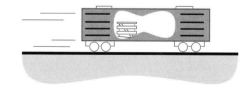

continued

A3. A ball swings in a horizontal circle at constant speed. (Consider a time interval in which the ball completes one full revolution.)

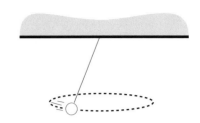

A4. A cannonball is shot with a speed of 40m/s at an angle of 45° as shown. (Consider the ball from the instant it leaves the cannon until just before it hits the ground.)

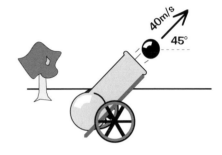

A5. A marble rolls along the floor and collides with a wall, rebounding with the same speed it had before. (Consider the marble while it is in contact with the wall.)

A6. A basketball is dropped from a height of 1.5m above the floor of the gym. After it bounces, it reaches a maximum height of 50cm. (Consider the basketball only during the time interval when it is touching the floor.)

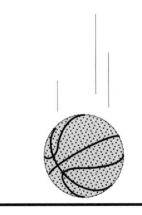

Reflection

Now that you have analyzed the forces, the momentum, and the impulses delivered in a variety of situations, you must think about how each concept relates to the others. In this Reflection, you are asked to seek patterns between each pair of concepts.

R1. For which situations is the momentum of the object the same throughout the entire time interval?

R2. Are there any forces that deliver <u>no</u> impulses during the specified time periods? Explain.

R3. In 5 of the 7 situations (including the example), there is a net force exerted on the object during the time period considered. Which five? Is momentum conserved in any of these cases?

R4. For which situations is the net impulse on the object zero? What other quantity is zero in <u>every one</u> of these cases? Is momentum conserved in each of these cases?

R5. In one of the situations, the net impulse is zero, but momentum is not constant throughout the time interval. In which situation does this happen? How does this happen?

R6. In which situations is the magnitude of the momentum the same at both the beginning and the end of the time interval? Is momentum the same as well? Explain why or why not.

Relating Momentum Ideas to Situations Having Two or More Objects

Purpose and Expected Outcome

Momentum is particularly useful in analyzing situations and solving problems involving more than one object. In this activity, you will examine situations in which two or more objects interact with each other. You will learn the value of defining a *system* of objects, and that even if you do not know the internal forces exerted on the objects in the system, you can often determine the behavior of the objects. You will learn also that even if you know how a force changes with position, dynamics is not particularly useful for determining the resulting motion.

Prior Experience / Knowledge Needed

You should know the definitions of impulse and momentum, and you should have some experience with the Impulse–Momentum Theorem ($\mathbf{J}_{net} = \Delta\mathbf{p}$).

SYSTEMS OF PARTICLES OR OBJECTS

It is often convenient to group objects together mentally and call them a *system*. In these cases, there is a definite "in" and a definite "out". Systems are usually chosen so that the forces exerted by outside objects are either non-existent (no external forces), or negligible, or balanced (no <u>net</u> external force), or constant and well behaved (such as friction or gravitation). Forces exerted by objects in a system by other objects in the system are termed *internal*, while forces exerted by objects outside the system are *external*.

Explanation of Activity and Example

For each of the situations below, answer the following questions.

(a) List all of the <u>external</u> forces exerted on the system. Describe any changes in the net force during the specified time interval.

(b) Does the system have an initial momentum? Describe any changes in its total momentum.

(c) Does the system experience a net impulse during the specified time period? Explain.

Example. Two carts are connected by a compressed spring, all at rest. Later, the two carts fly apart with constant speed. Consider the two carts and  the spring from the time they are released until the time the carts are moving the fastest.

Answers:

(a) *Ignoring friction, there is a gravitational and a normal force on each cart exerted by the earth. If the spring is assumed massless, there are no external forces on it.*

(b) *Initially, the system has zero momentum. The total momentum does not change with time.*

(c) *There is no net impulse delivered to the system. The gravitational and normal forces balance.*

A1. A fireworks device is shot into the air and explodes at its maximum height, sending out debris in all directions. Consider the fireworks during the explosion.

A2. Two blocks are connected by a light string and frictionless pulley as shown. Consider the two blocks and the string from the time they are released from rest until just before the heavier block hits the ground.

A3. A ball is dropped from rest, bounces off the floor, and returns to its original position. Consider the ball and the earth (as a system) from the time the ball is released until it returns to its initial position.

continued

A4. A lump of clay is dropped onto a moving cart from just above the cart. Consider the clay and the cart from the instant the clay first makes contact with the cart until they are both moving with the same velocity.

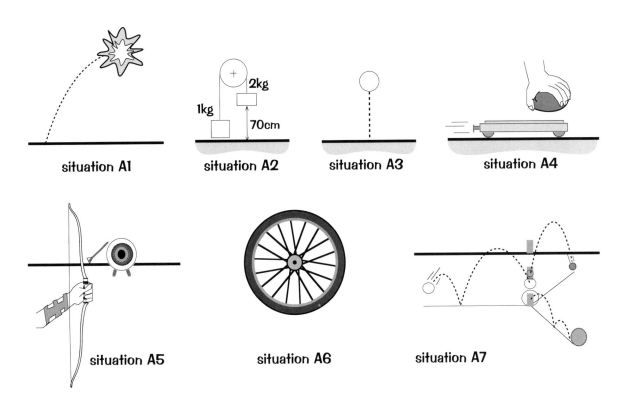

situation A1

2kg
1kg
70cm

situation A2

situation A3

situation A4

situation A5

situation A6

situation A7

A5. At camp, a young woman shoots an arrow toward a circular target. Consider the bow and arrow from the instant the arrow is released from rest until just before it loses contact with the bow.

A6. A wheel is spinning on a fixed horizontal axle, eventually slowing to a stop in 70 seconds. Consider the wheel while it is spinning.

A7. Three balls are stacked with the lightest one on top and the heaviest one on the bottom. They are released from rest from 1 meter above the ground and follow the trajectories shown. Consider the three balls from the time they are released until just after they bounce off the ground the first time.

Reflection

R1. For which situations is the total momentum conserved (that is, does not change during the time interval)? For which situations is a component of the total momentum conserved? Explain.

R2. Consider the situations in which the total momentum is conserved. Examine the forces exerted in each of these situations. What is true about the forces in all these situations?

R3. Consider those situations in which total momentum is <u>not</u> conserved. What is similar about the forces exerted in these situations? How was the total momentum changed? Is it possible to choose the system differently so that the total momentum <u>is</u> conserved? If so, what would this new system be in each case?

77

Reasoning with Impulse and Momentum Ideas

Purpose and Expected Outcome

Even though we often do not know very much about the forces between interacting objects, we can still understand much of their behavior using momentum ideas. In this activity, you will examine situations in which objects interact. You will use either the Impulse–Momentum Theorem or the principle of Conservation of Momentum to analyze and reason about the problem situations.

Prior Experience / Knowledge Needed

You should know the definitions of momentum and impulse, and you should be familiar with how these ideas are used to describe the interaction between pairs of objects. You should be familiar with the Impulse–Momentum Theorem, as well as the conditions under which the total momentum of a system of objects is conserved.

Explanation of Activity

This activity contains two parts. Answer each of the questions below, and provide an explanation of how you used momentum and impulse ideas to find your answer.

PART A: Motion in One Dimension

A1. Two identical cars are found after having collided on a slippery road. The cars are stationary, and their bumpers are locked together. There are no signs that either car skidded before or after the collision. What can you conclude about the accident? What additional evidence could you look for to support your analysis? Explain.

A2. A golf ball, a softball, and a basketball are dropped at the same instant from a fourth-story window. One second later, which ball has the largest speed? Which has the largest momentum? Which has the smallest momentum? Explain.

A3. An object collides with a second object at rest. Is it possible for <u>resulting</u> momentum of the second object to be larger than the <u>initial</u> momentum of the first object? If not, explain why it is not possible for this to happen. If it is possible, give an example.

A4. A marble rolls along a straight horizontal track at constant speed and collides with a second marble at rest. The plot on the right shows how the momentum of the first marble changes with time. On a copy of this graph, sketch how the momentum of the other marble changes with time. Explain how you made your sketch.

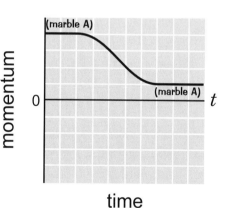

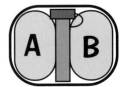

B1. An explosive device is made up of two moderately heavy canisters of material, one on each side of a lightweight explosive as shown. The device is programmed to explode the instant it reaches its maximum height, and is weighted so that the canisters will be projected horizontally by the explosion. The device is launched straight up into the air and explodes. Later, canister A is found on the ground 30m from the launch site, and canister B is found 40m from the launch site. What can you conclude based on these observations? Explain.

B2. The nucleus of fermium-256 has a mass of about 256amu, and is radioactively unstable. A Fm-256 nucleus is traveling to the right with a speed of 30km/s when it decays into a uranium-238 nucleus and an oxygen-18 nucleus. Is it possible for the oxygen nucleus to travel in a direction perpendicular to the initial direction of the Fm nucleus? If not, explain why not, and if so, indicate how it is possible.

B3. A truck having a mass of 2000kg and a speed of 25mph (about 11m/s) is traveling toward an intersection in which a small car is stuck in a pool of oil. The truck driver tries to stop but the brakes have no effect on the truck's motion. After the collision, the truck moves with a speed of 10mph (about 4.5m/s) at an angle of 30° from its initial direction. What can be determined about the car involved in the collision? (For example, can we determine its mass? its final speed? its direction of motion? its momentum? a component of its momentum?)

B4. A spy satellite has escaped earth's gravitation and is at rest in space. To prevent it from being captured by a hostile government, it must be destroyed. The resulting explosion creates three fragments. Two of the fragments travel along the paths shown, and are equidistant from the explosion site at the instant shown.

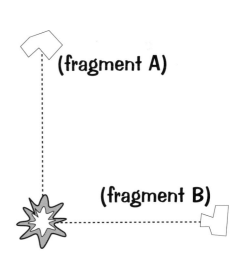

(a) What can you say about the velocities of these two fragments after the explosion? Are they constant or changing with time?

(b) Explain why the path of the third fragment (C) <u>must</u> lie in the plane formed by the paths of the other two.

(c) What is the path of C when the masses of A and B are equal?

(d) On a copy of this figure, indicate the range of possible paths for fragment C, and label your possible paths according to which fragment, A or B, is heavier.

Reflection

All the questions in this activity could be answered using either Conservation of Momentum or the Impulse–Momentum Theorem. In this Reflection, you should consider the factors that lead you to choose one over the other.

R1. For which questions did you use the principle of Conservation of Momentum? For which did you use the Impulse–Momentum Theorem? For which <u>could</u> you have used both? What caused you to choose one method over the other?

R2. In part A, how many separate relationships does momentum conservation provide? In part B? How does the number of relationships compare to the number of dimensions in each part?

R3. Create a situation in which momentum is conserved in one direction but not another. How do you know that momentum is not conserved in one of the directions?

78

Solving Problems Using Momentum Principles

Purpose and Expected Outcome

Now that you have covered momentum and impulse ideas, and know how they can be used to analyze physical situations, it is time to use momentum principles to solve problems. However, some problems still require dynamics. In this activity, you will learn how to bring together analysis and problem solving skills to first decide how a problem should be solved, and then to answer specific questions about the motion and behavior of different objects.

Prior Experience / Knowledge Needed

You should be familiar with kinematics, Newton's laws, dynamics, the definitions of impulse and momentum, the Impulse–Momentum Theorem, and the principle of Conservation of Momentum. You should have experience analyzing physical situations.

Explanation of Activity

There are two parts to this activity. In the first part, all the problems are solved using momentum and impulse ideas. In the second part, you must first decide <u>how</u> you will solve each problem before actually solving it.

PART A: Solving Problems Using Momentum and Impulse

For each problem, solve for the desired unknown using one or more of the following:

- the definitions of impulse and momentum;
- the Impulse–Momentum Theorem; and
- Conservation of Momentum.

Keep in mind that in some cases <u>you</u> must decide what the best choice is for the system.

A1. A 1kg cart carries a 600g lump of clay securely on its top. The combination is traveling at 50cm/s when it collides with another 1kg cart at rest. After the collision, the lighter cart is observed to travel at 60cm/s.

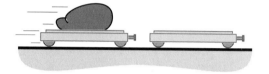

(a) What is the velocity of the heavier cart after the collision?

(b) What impulse is delivered to the lighter cart during the collision?

(c) What impulse is delivered to the clay during the collision?

A2. A cue ball strikes a billiard ball which is initially at rest. The contact point is the origin of the coordinate system shown in the diagram. Also shown are the paths and velocities of the balls after the collision.

(a) What is the velocity of the cue ball before the collision?

(b) If the mass of the billiard ball is 125g, what is the impulse delivered to it by the cue ball?

(c) If the balls are in contact for only 0.002s, what is the average force exerted on the cue ball by the billiard ball?

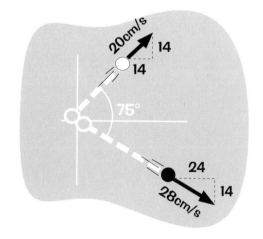

PART B: Deciding Problem-Solving Approach

For each problem, first describe <u>how</u> you will solve the problem, and then solve for the desired unknown using your chosen approach.

B1. A 25g marble travels to the right along a grooved track at constant velocity. At $t = 0s$, it collides with a 40g steel ball which is also moving at constant velocity. The graphs of their momenta versus time are shown to the right. (1ms = 0.001s)

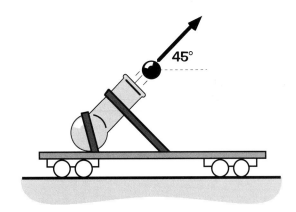

(a) What are the initial velocities of the marble and the steel ball?

(b) What is the initial momentum of the marble–ball system?

(c) What is the momentum of the steel ball at $t = 0.5ms$?

(d) On a copy of this graph, sketch the momentum of the steel ball for $t > 0s$. What is the final velocity of the steel ball?

(e) What is the impulse delivered to the steel ball during the collision?

B2. A cannon is securely attached to a flatbed railroad car as shown, and fired with the system at rest. The explosion lasts about $^{1}/_{20}$ second, after which the cannonball is observed to travel at 45°, and the railroad car is observed to travel at 14cm/s. The cannonball weighs about 75lb (mass about 34kg), and the cannon and railroad car have a combined weight of about 15,000lb (mass about 6800kg). You may ignore the effects of friction and air resistance throughout.

(a) What is the horizontal component of the cannonball's initial velocity?

(b) What impulse is delivered to the railroad car by the tracks?

(c) How far apart are the railroad car and cannonball when the cannonball lands?

(d) Which has the larger momentum when the cannonball lands, the cannonball or the car–cannon system? Explain.

Reflection

In this Reflection, you should consider the role of thinking about and analyzing a situation before solving a problem.

R1. How important would you say that thinking about the concepts is for efficient and successful problem solving? In what ways have critical thinking skills changed how you approach problems?

R2. Under what conditions is Conservation of Momentum a useful problem-solving principle?

R3. In problem A1, <u>which</u> object delivers an impulse to the clay? During what time period does this occur? Explain.

R4. In problem B1, a classmate is not convinced that the grooved track is both horizontal and straight. Perhaps it is curved in some way. What do you think? Is there enough information given in the problem for you to determine if the track is perfectly straight? Explain why or why not. Is there enough information to determine if the track is perfectly horizontal? Explain why or why not.

Summarizing and Structuring Momentum and Impulse Ideas

Purpose and Expected Outcome

In this activity you will create a summary of all the concepts associated with momentum and impulse, then you will construct a concept map with them. This activity will help you remember and consider these concepts when analyzing situations and solving problems. You should keep this summary and concept map, along with all previous ones, for future reference.

You will also add to your list of valuable techniques, skills, procedures, and strategies for solving problems.

Prior Experience / Knowledge Needed

You should know the concepts associated with momentum, and you should have some experience reasoning and solving problems with momentum ideas.

Explanation of Activity

There are four parts to this activity.

PART A: Summarizing Momentum Concepts

Explain in your own words each of the following concepts or principles, and describe how they are related to each other and to other physical quantities. Express each concept or principle as a mathematical relationship, and make sure each symbol in each relationship is defined.

A1.   Impulse

A2.   Momentum

A3.   Impulse–Momentum Theorem

A4.   Conservation of Momentum

PART B: Comparing Summaries

Compare your statements from part A with those of your classmates and rephrase them so that everyone agrees.

PART C: Creating a Concept Map

In a group or as a class, create a concept map of these ideas showing how they are related to each other and to ideas covered previously in the course.

PART D: Adding More Problem-Solving Ideas

As a class, make any necessary additions to your sorted list of problem-solving ideas.

Recording Your Thoughts about Energy

Purpose and Expected Outcome

Before starting a new topic, it is often a good idea to make everyone (including your teacher) aware of how you and your classmates think about the new subject. This activity will help you to recognize when your way of thinking about energy is different than the physicist's way. In this activity, you will consider a variety of situations and will talk about the energy content in each situation. You will learn that within your class there are many different views about energy.

Prior Experience / Knowledge Needed

None.

Explanation of Activity

There are two parts to this activity.

PART A: Identifying Energy

For each of the situations below, first indicate whether or not energy <u>as you understand it to be</u> is present. Then give your reasons for your answer.

Group A1:

(a) A ball sits at rest on a horizontal surface.

(b) A ball sits at rest on a small hill.

(c) A ball rolls along a horizontal surface.

(d) A ball sits at the bottom of a small valley.

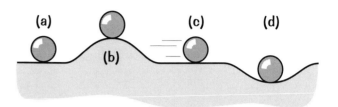

Group A2:

(a) A ball is held at rest above a horizontal surface.

(b) A ball falls toward a horizontal surface.

(c) A ball is bouncing on the floor. At the instant shown, it has reached its maximum height and is about to fall back down again.

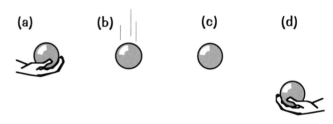

(d) A ball is held at rest above a horizontal surface at a lower height than the others.

Group A3:

(a) A person runs along the sidewalk.

(b) A person pushes a wagon up a hill.

(c) A person holds a wagon at rest on a hill.

(d) A person is pushing a wagon along the sidewalk.

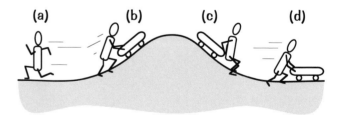

continued

Group A4:

(a) A ball is used to compress a spring.

(b) A ball falls toward a spring.

(c) A ball sits at rest on a spring.

(d) A ball sits at rest next to a spring.

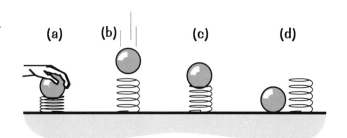

Group A5:

(a) A tray of ice cubes is in the freezer.

(b) A glass of water is put into the freezer.

(c) A tray of ice cubes melts on a hot day.

(d) A pot of water is boiling on the stove.

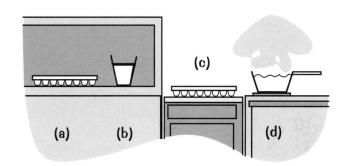

Group A6:

(a) A battery, bulb, and two wires sit on the floor.

(b) A battery, bulb, and two wires are connected such that the light bulb glows.

(c) A light bulb is plugged into a wall socket and switched on.

(d) A light bulb is plugged into a wall socket, but the switch is left off.

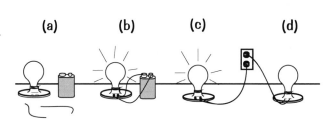

PART B: Identifying <u>Changes</u> in Energy

For each of the processes described below, first indicate whether energy <u>as you understand it to be</u> is increasing, decreasing, or staying the same. Then give your reasons for your answer.

B1. A ball rolls along a horizontal surface.

B2. A ball rolls down a small hill.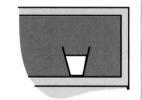

B3. A large block of ice is melting under the hot sun.

B4. A pot of water is boiling on the stove.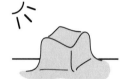

B5. A glass of water is put into the freezer of a refrigerator, where it eventually turns into ice.

B6. A person is running.

B7. A person is sitting under the hot sun.

B8. Two balls are used to compress a spring (top) and are released (bottom).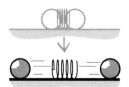

B9. A battery and two wires are used to turn on a light bulb.

B10. Baking soda and vinegar are mixed together to simulate a volcanic eruption.

Reflection

R1. List all the types of energy that you are familiar with. For each type, give an example of an object or situation having this type of energy.

R2. How do you recognize when energy is increasing? Does your method depend upon the type of energy? Explain.

R3. Do you suppose there is any relationship between force and energy? Explain. Is there any relationship between energy and motion? Explain. Is there any relationship between energy and position? Explain.

Relating Forces to the Motion of Objects

Purpose and Expected Outcome

In previous MOP activities, you have seen the limitations of dynamics and you have seen how impulse and momentum ideas can be used to understand situations and solve problems when dynamics cannot. In this activity you will learn how two new ideas, *work* and *kinetic energy*, can be used to study the motion of objects.

Prior Experience / Knowledge Needed

You should be able to solve kinematics and dynamics problems.

Explanation of Activity

You will solve dynamics problems, then use the results to relate various physical quantities. For the object specified in each process, first determine:

(a) $\mathbf{F}_{net}$ the net force exerted on the object (a vector),

(b) $\mathbf{d}$ its displacement (also a vector),

(c) $F_{net,\parallel}$ the <u>component</u> of the net force parallel to the direction of motion (a number with units),

(d) d the magnitude of the displacement (a scalar),

(e) M the mass of the object, and

(f) v_i, v_f its initial and final speeds.

Put these into a table. Then, using these quantities, (g) compute $F_{net,\parallel}\, d$ and $\Delta(Mv^2)$ for each process. Throughout these situations, use $g = 10\text{N/kg}$ and ignore air resistance.

Note: $\mathbf{F}_{net}$ and $\mathbf{d}$ are <u>vectors</u>, therefore you must indicate their directions.

A1. A 0.3kg ball is dropped from rest and lands one second later. Consider the ball from the time it is released until just before it hits the ground.

A2. A 4kg toy car rolls at a constant speed, until someone applies a horizontal force of 12N, as shown. It takes only 1 second to stop the car. Consider the car only while the person is stopping it.

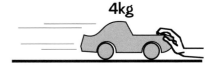

A3. A 12kg wagon is pulled with a 10N force as shown. Its initial speed is 1m/s, and it is pulled for 6 seconds.

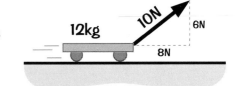

continued

	Situation	$\mathbf{F}_{net}$ (N)	**d** (m)	$F_{net,\|}$ (N)	d (m)	M (kg)	v_i (m/s)	v_f (m/s)	$F_{net,\|}\,d$ (N-m)	$\Delta(Mv^2)$ (kg-m²/s²)
A1.	dropped ball	3 ↓		3		0.3	0			
A2.	rolling toy car			–12		4		0	–18	
A3.	pulled wagon					12	1			

Reflection

R1. Under what conditions is $F_{net,\|}$ negative? Explain.

R2. What is the relationship between the product $F_{net,\|}d$ and the <u>change</u> in the quantity Mv^2? Are the units for these two quantities equivalent? (In other words, is 1N × 1m equal to 1kg × (1m/s)²?) Explain why or why not.

R3. When the product $F_{net,\|}d$ is positive, how does the speed change? Explain.

R4. When the product $F_{net,\|}d$ is negative, how does the speed change? Explain.

R5. If the product $F_{net,\|}d$ is zero, how do you think the speed would change? Explain. Describe two examples of situations for which this product is zero. How does the speed change in your examples? Is your prediction correct? Comment.

Summary

The previous examples suggest that when the force is constant, the product $F_{net,\|}d$ is equal to one-half the change in Mv^2. This is similar to what happened with impulse and momentum: the net <u>impulse</u> delivered to an object is equal to the change in its <u>momentum</u>. The product $F_{net,\|}d$ is the *total work* and $\frac{1}{2}Mv^2$ is the *kinetic energy*. Therefore, the total <u>work</u> done on an object is equal to the change in its <u>kinetic energy</u>.

Relating Work to Forces and Displacements

Purpose and Expected Outcome

In this activity, you will learn how to apply the definition of work in a variety of situations.

Prior Experience / Knowledge Needed

You should understand forces and displacements. You should know how to find or identify the component of a vector along a particular direction.

WORK

The work W_F done by a constant force **F** exerted through a displacement **d** is:

$$W_F \equiv F\,d\,\cos\theta \qquad\qquad \text{definition of work}$$

where
F = magnitude of the force **F**
d = magnitude of the displacement **d**
θ = <u>smallest</u> angle between **F** and **d**

The displacement is always measured as the change in position of the point at which the force is exerted. So for example, if we have a rope attached to the front of a wagon, the picture would look like this. As the front of the wagon moves from point A to point B, the displacement **d** is the vector connecting the two points.

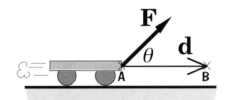

Here are two alternative forms of the work:

$$W_F = F_{\parallel}\,d \qquad - \text{ and } - \qquad W_F = F\,d_{\parallel}$$

where
$F_{\parallel}$ = component of the force **F** parallel to the displacement **d**
$d_{\parallel}$ = component of the displacement **d** parallel to the force **F**

In any particular situation, <u>you</u> must decide which form is easiest or most convenient to apply. If the force is not constant, you must consider displacements small enough so that the force can be treated as being constant.

Explanation of Activity and Example

Six situations are described below. For each situation, (a) determine the <u>sign</u> (+, 0, or −) of the work done by the specified force, and (b) provide an explanation for your answer.

Example. A ball falls to the ground under the influence of gravitation.

Answers:

(a) *The work done by gravitation is positive (+).*

(b) *The gravitational force and the displacement are in the same direction (straight down), so the angle between them is $\theta = 0°$. Therefore $Fd\cos\theta$ is positive.*

---

continued

A1. A ball flies straight up into the air but slows down due to gravitation.

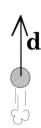

A2. A wagon (moving left) is pulled by a constant force as shown.

A3. A toy car is stopped by an applied force.

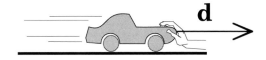

A4. A book lies at rest with a force exerted as shown.

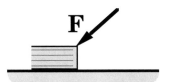

A5. A ball is thrown between two people. (Consider only gravitation.)

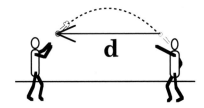

A6. A ball swings on a string due to gravitation. (Consider only gravitation.)

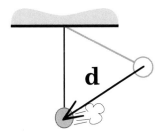

Reflection

R1. Which forms for the definition of work did you use to find the sign of the work? Which did you use most often? Which form do you find easiest to apply? Explain.

R2. Under what conditions is the work done by a particular force equal to zero?

R3. In situations A2, A3, and A4, what is the sign of the work done by the normal force? Explain.

R4. (a) Describe a situation in which the *x*-component of a force is positive, yet the component of the same force parallel to the displacement is negative. Use a drawing to explain your answer.

(b) Can you determine the <u>sign</u> of the work done by the force described in part (a)? If so, what is the sign? If not, explain why not.

(c) Describe a situation in which the horizontal component of a force is negative, yet the component of the same force parallel to the displacement is positive. Draw the situation.

(d) Can you determine the <u>sign</u> of the work done by the force described in part (c)? If so, what is the sign? If not, explain why not.

Recognizing the Presence of Work

Purpose and Expected Outcome

Many terms we use in physics are also used in everyday language. Usually, the definition of a term in physics is similar (that's why it is chosen) but in fact different (that's why it is confusing). In this activity we provide the physics definition of the term *work*. After completing this activity, you will understand better the difference between its physics meaning and its everyday meaning, and you will recognize those physical situations in which work (in the physics sense!) is being done.

Prior Experience / Knowledge Needed

You should know the definition of *work* and be able to apply it in different situations. You should know how to find the component of a vector along a particular direction.

"TOTAL" WORK

The *total work* is simply the sum of the amounts of work done by <u>all</u> the forces exerted on an object. Recall that the work done by any particular force depends on the displacement of the point at which the force is exerted. If the object is rigid (i.e., does not deform) and also does not rotate, then every point in the object has the same displacement, and we can use the net force to find the total work:

$$W_{\text{total}} = F_{\text{net}}\, d\, \cos\theta$$

(only true when the object does not deform <u>and</u> does not rotate)

where F_{net} = magnitude of the net force $\mathbf{F}_{\text{net}}$
          d = magnitude of the displacement of the object $\mathbf{d}$
          θ = <u>smallest</u> angle between $\mathbf{F}_{\text{net}}$ and $\mathbf{d}$

This can be rewritten in two alternative forms:

$$W_{\text{total}} = F_{\text{net},\parallel}\, d \qquad - \text{and} - \qquad W_{\text{total}} = F_{\text{net}}\, d_{\parallel}$$

where $F_{\text{net},\parallel}$ = <u>component</u> of $\mathbf{F}_{\text{net}}$ parallel to $\mathbf{d}$
          $d_{\parallel}$ = <u>component</u> of $\mathbf{d}$ parallel to $\mathbf{F}_{\text{net}}$

In actual situations, <u>you</u> must decide which form is easiest to apply.

Explanation of Activity and Example

For each of the objects specified below, (a) identify <u>all</u> the forces exerted on the object and determine the <u>sign</u> (+, 0, or −) of the work done by each force, and (b) determine the sign (+, 0, or −) of the <u>total</u> work done on the object. Be prepared to discuss and explain your answers.

Example. A toy car is stopped by an applied force as shown.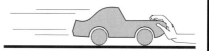

> ***Answers:***
>
> (a) *Gravitation does no work. The normal force does no work. The applied force does negative work. Air resistance does a negligible amount of work.*
>
> (b) *The total work is negative. (**Explanation:** The net force is roughly constant and always opposite the displacement.)*

---

continued

A1. A monkey climbs up a rope. Consider only the forces on the <u>rope</u>.

A2. A skydiver (who has not yet opened her parachute) falls at constant velocity. Consider only the forces on the <u>skydiver</u>.

A3. A person holds a bag of groceries while riding up an elevator at constant speed. Consider only the forces on the <u>bag of groceries</u>.

A4. A cart is pushed by a compressed spring. Consider only the forces on the <u>cart</u> as the spring expands.

A5. A horizontal force is applied to compress a spring. Consider only the forces on the <u>spring</u>.

A6. A person throws a ball into the air. The ball hits a wall as shown above and then hits the ground. Consider only the forces on the <u>ball</u> from its maximum height until just before it hits the ground.

A7. Three roller coaster cars full of people ride along the curved track shown above. Consider only the <u>cars full of people</u> from the maximum height until the end of the ride.

A8. A 2kg block is attached to a string wrapped around a 3kg pulley and released from rest. Consider only the forces on the <u>pulley</u>.

A9. A dictionary slides across a table top. Consider only the forces on the <u>table</u>.

Reflection

R1. In situation A1, does the rope do work on the monkey? Explain.

R2. A person standing still holds a heavy bag of groceries. Is this person doing work? If so, is this work positive or negative? Explain. Now the same person is riding in an elevator going upward at constant speed. Is this person doing work now? If so, is it positive work or negative work? Explain. Now the elevator is going downward at constant speed. Is the person doing work? If so, is it positive or negative? Explain.

R3. A weight lifter bench-presses 80kg for 10 reps then returns the weights to their original position. Does the weight lifter do any total work on the weights? Explain. If so, exactly when?

R4. Under what conditions does a constant force do no work? Explain.

R5. In situation A3, does the person do work on the elevator? If so, is it positive or negative? Explain. Does the elevator do work on the bag of groceries? Explain.

Integration of Ideas

For each of the forces listed below, give an example in which the force does positive work on an object. Then, give an example in which the force does negative work on an object and an example in which it does no work. Some examples have been provided already.

	Force	Force does ... positive work	negative work	no work
I1.	gravitation			A ball is thrown and caught at the same height above the ground.
I2.	spring force		A ball lands on a vertical spring and eventually comes to rest on it.	
I3.	tension force	A wagon is pulled by a rope along a sidewalk.		
I4.	normal force		A toy car hits a block sitting on a carpet. (If the block slides, negative work is done on the car by the normal force exerted by the block.)	
I5.	static friction force			A book sits at rest on an inclined plane.

Comparing the Work Done by Forces

Purpose and Expected Outcome

In this activity, you will use your knowledge of forces and motion to determine the signs and relative magnitudes of the work done by different forces in different situations.

Prior Experience / Knowledge Needed

You should know the common forces and how they depend on physical characteristics. You should know the definition of work, and be able to apply it.

Explanation of Activity

For each of the groups of situations below, put in increasing order the work done by the specified force. (Start with the most negative, and end with the most positive.) Indicate if two or more amounts of work are exactly the same. Be prepared to discuss your answers.

Group A1: Five marbles travel over 5 pieces of felt arranged on the floor as shown below. Arrange the five situations according to the work done <u>by the felt on the marble</u>. **Note:** <u>None</u> of the marbles <u>ever</u> comes to rest on the felt. (**Hints:** What type of force does the felt exert on the marble? How does this force depend upon the mass of the marble?)

(a) The marble slows down on a piece of felt.

(b) The felt is thinner and lighter than in (a), causing the marble to slow down less than in (a).

(c) The marble is twice the mass of the marble in (a). It is observed to slow down at the same rate as in (a).

(d) The felt is twice as long as the piece in (a).

(e) The marble hits a fixed wall and passes over the same piece of felt a second time.

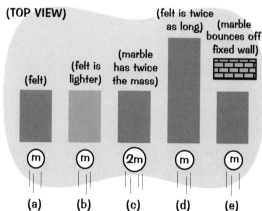

Group A2: A cart is <u>initially moving to the right</u> on a horizontal surface. In five different ways (shown at right) a horizontal force is applied to the cart as it travels from $x = 0\text{m}$ to $x = 2\text{m}$. Consider the work done by the <u>applied force</u>.

(a) The force is constant at 2N.

(b) The force is constant at –2N.

(c) The force is constant at –2N for 1m, then constant at 2N for 1m.

(d) The force increases uniformly from 0N to 2N.

(e) The force increases uniformly from 0N to 4N.

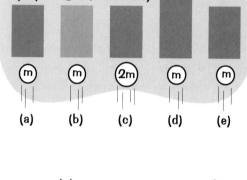

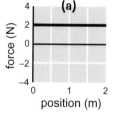

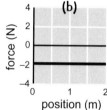

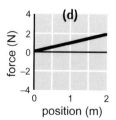

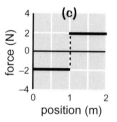

Group A3: A cart <u>is initially moving to the right</u> on a horizontal surface. In six different ways (shown below) a force is applied to the cart between $x = 0$cm and $x = 40$cm. The magnitude of the force is the same in every case. Consider the work done by the <u>applied force</u>.

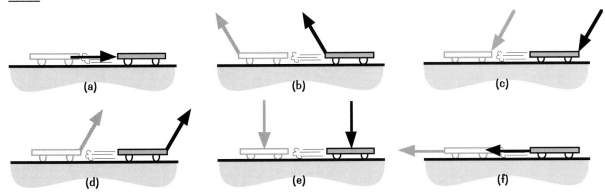

Group A4: Consider the work done by <u>gravitation</u> on the ball in each of the following situations.

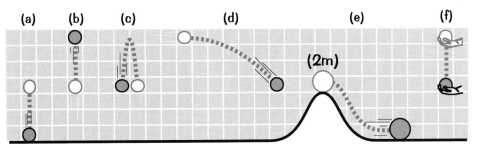

(a) A ball falls a distance D.

(b) A ball goes up a distance D.

(c) A ball goes up a distance D, then falls back down a distance D.

(d) A ball moves horizontally $2D$ as it falls a distance D.

(e) A ball having twice the mass of the others rolls down a small hill of height D.

(f) A ball is slowly lowered by hand a distance D.

Reflection

R1. Can one object do work on a second object without the second object doing work on the first? Explain. If your answer is yes, give an example.

R2. A 2kg object falls toward the earth and lands 4 seconds later. Is work done by the gravitational force of the object on the earth? Explain why or why not. (**Hints:** Is there a gravitational force on the earth? Is it constant? Does the earth move?)

R3. Compare the work done <u>by the person on a crate</u> in the following two cases. Ignore air resistance.

Case A. The crate is pulled for 2 meters at constant speed using a rope held at an angle as shown.

Case B. The <u>same</u> crate is pushed at an angle as shown at constant speed for 2 meters.

In which case (*A* or *B*) is the work done by the person larger, or are they the same? Explain.

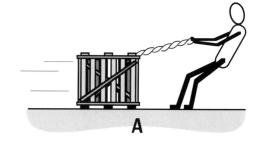

R4. Under what circumstances is the work done by a force equal to zero? Give at least three different general conditions for which the work done is zero.

Minds•On Physics Activity 85

Computing the Work Done by Forces

Purpose and Expected Outcome

In this activity, you will learn how to determine numerical values for the work done by different forces.

Prior Experience / Knowledge Needed

You should know the common forces and how they depend on physical characteristics. You should know the definition of work, and be able to apply it. You should know how to estimate the work done by a non-constant force.

WORK DONE BY NON-CONSTANT FORCES

Most of the relationships you have used so far assumed that the force exerted on an object was constant. In many cases, the force is not constant. For instance, for an object on a string moving in a horizontal circle, the tension force has the same magnitude, but its direction is constantly changing. The spring force depends on its compression or extension, so its magnitude is constantly changing. When the force is not constant, we simply consider displacements so small that the force can be treated as constant throughout the displacement. The work is calculated the same way as before. The total work done during a process is the sum of the work done during each small displacement. If we graph $F_{\parallel}$ versus distance traveled s, the total work done by the force between points A and B is the area between the graph and the horizontal axis, as shown in gray.

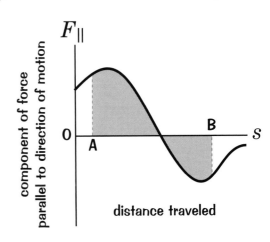

Explanation of Activity and Example

Compute or estimate the work done by the specified forces in each of the problems below.

Example. A 5kg cat is sleeping on a light blanket when little Sophia (all 14kg of her) decides to pick up the blanket and take it. The coefficient of sliding friction between the blanket and the coffee table is 0.12, and the coefficient of static friction between her feet and the floor is 0.5. How much work does Sophia do to move the blanket (and cat!) 1 meter?

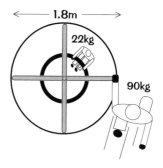

Answer: *The only force exerted by Sophia that does work is the applied force to the blanket. Assuming she pulls at constant speed, the applied force is equal to the friction force exerted on the blanket, which is equal to 6N. The applied force and the displacement are both horizontal and in the same direction, so:*

$$W_{applied} = F_{applied}\, d = (6N) \times (1m) = 6J.$$

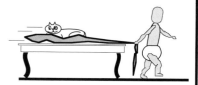

A1. A father pushes his daughter on a merry-go-round with a horizontal force of 40N as shown. How much work is done by the father on the merry-go-round after two complete revolutions?

A2. A 40kg child swings from one tree to the next using a rope attached high up in one of the trees. The distance between the trees is 5m, and the child's initial and final height is 3.4m.

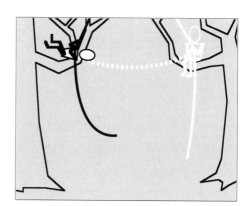

(a) How much work is done on the child by the gravitational force?

(b) How much work is done on the child by the rope?

(c) If the child falls out of the tree, how much work is done by gravitation?

continued

A3. A 100g ball rolls down a rough, 30° incline.

    (a) How much work is done by the gravitational force on the ball?

    (b) How much work is done by the normal force on the ball?

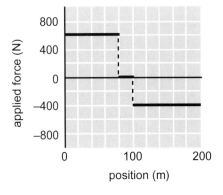

A4. A locomotive engine exerts a horizontal force on a railroad car through a distance of 200 meters using an applied force that changes with position as shown to the right.

    (a) How much work is done by the engine on the car in the first 100 meters?

    (b) How much work is done by the engine on the car over the entire 200 meters?

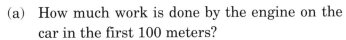

A5. A horizontal spring with a spring constant of 10N/cm is used to push a 200g toy car. The maximum compression of the spring is 2cm.

    (a) Make a sketch of the spring force versus position. Be as quantitative as possible. (And be sure to label your axes.)

    (b) How much work is done by the spring after the car is released?

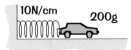

A6. Jesse is pulling a 60kg crate across a floor having a coefficient of sliding friction of 0.35 using a rope angled as shown. He is moving at $1/3$ m/s throughout.

    (a) How much work does Jesse do on the crate every <u>meter</u> that he moves?

    (b) How much work does Jesse do on the crate every <u>second</u> that he moves?

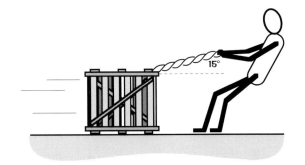

Reflection

R1. Give an example of a situation in which the net force is opposite the direction of motion. Does the object speed up or slow down in this situation? Is this always true when the net force is opposite the direction of motion? Explain.

R2. Give an example of a situation in which the net force is perpendicular to the direction of motion. Does the object speed up or slow down in this situation? Is this aways true when the net force is perpendicular to the direction of motion? Explain.

R3. The total work done on a particular object is positive. Can you predict whether it speeds up or slows down? Explain. Can you predict what happens to its direction of motion? Explain.

R4. Re-consider situation A3. Are there any forces other than gravitation and a normal force on the ball as it rolls down the incline? Explain why you think so. Do any of these forces do work on the ball? Explain.

Recognizing and Comparing Kinetic Energy

Purpose and Expected Outcome

This activity will familiarize you with the definition of *kinetic energy*. After completing this activity, you should be able to recognize kinetic energy in complex situations, and you will know when it changes and when it does not change during a process. You will see that in some cases the velocity changes but the kinetic energy does not. You should appreciate the similarities and differences between kinetic energy and momentum.

Prior Experience / Knowledge Needed

You should be familiar with the definition of work, and be able to compute the work done by a constant force.

As we saw in an earlier activity, the *total work* done on a rigid, non-rotating body is equal to <u>one-half</u> the change in the quantity Mv^2. If we think of the total work as an amount of energy given to the object, then $\Delta(\frac{1}{2}Mv^2)$ is the change in the energy of the object. Because this form of energy depends on the speed of the object, we call it the *kinetic* energy. We define the kinetic energy in a very particular way, because this quantity comes into play in a wide variety of situations.

For a <u>point</u> object (zero volume) having mass m and speed v, its kinetic energy is defined to be:

$$E_K \equiv \frac{1}{2}mv^2$$

definition of kinetic energy
for a point object having mass m and speed v

For a collection of point objects, the total kinetic energy is the sum of the kinetic energies of all of its parts:

$$E_{K,\text{total}} \equiv \frac{1}{2}m_a v_a{}^2 + \frac{1}{2}m_b v_b{}^2 + \ldots$$

definition of <u>total</u> kinetic energy
for a collection of point objects, $a, b, \ldots$

For a non-deformable (rigid), non-rotating object, every part is moving with exactly the same speed, so we can add up all the kinetic energies of all the parts to get:

$$E_{K,\text{total}} = \frac{1}{2}Mv^2$$

(for a rigid, non-rotating object
having mass M and speed v)

This is exactly the quantity that changed in the earlier activity. For any particular situation, <u>you</u> must decide how to apply the definition to determine the total kinetic energy. Note that kinetic energy is a scalar quantity, and therefore has <u>no</u> direction associated with it.

Explanation of Activity

For each situation below, you will compare the kinetic energy and the momentum.

A1. Two identical minivans (1600kg each) are traveling in opposite directions with the same speed of 90km/h (25m/s).

(a) What is the total momentum of the two minivans?

(b) What is the total kinetic energy of the two minivans?

continued

A2. Two identical race cars travel at the same constant speed v. One is going around an oval track as shown, and the other is traveling on a long, straight highway.

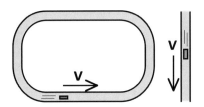

    (a) When, if ever, do the two cars have the same momentum?

    (b) When, if ever, do the two cars have the same kinetic energy?

A3. A certain truck has three times the mass, but only half the speed, of a small car.

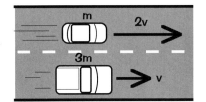

    (a) Which vehicle has the larger momentum? Explain.

    (b) Which vehicle has the larger kinetic energy? Explain.

A4. Two marbles are used to compress a spring and released from rest.

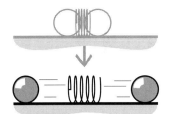

    (a) Does the total momentum of the two marbles remain constant? Explain.

    (b) Does the total kinetic energy of the two marbles remain constant? Explain.

A5. A 150g superball hits a wall traveling at 80cm/s and rebounds with exactly the same speed.

    (a) What is the superball's change in momentum as a result of hitting the wall?

    (b) What is the superball's change in kinetic energy as a result of hitting the wall?

A6. Consider the gas molecules inside your classroom.

    (a) Do the gas molecules have a zero or non-zero total momentum? Explain.

    (b) Do the gas molecules have a zero or non-zero total kinetic energy? Explain.

continued

A7. A simple mobile is made by attaching four small balls (0.1kg each) to the ends of two very light rods as shown. The mobile spins counterclockwise with each ball moving at 0.15m/s.

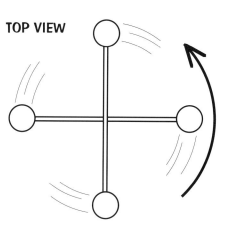

TOP VIEW

(a) What is the kinetic energy of each ball? What is the total kinetic energy of the four balls? Does the kinetic energy stay the same as the mobile is spinning? Explain.

(b) What is the total momentum of the four balls? Does the total momentum stay the same? Explain.

(c) Is there a net force exerted on any one of the balls? Is it constant? Is there total work being done on any of the balls as they move through ¼ revolution?

A8. A bicycle wheel is spinning around a fixed axle.

(a) Does the wheel have a zero or non-zero total momentum? Explain.

(b) Does the wheel have a zero or non-zero total kinetic energy? Explain.

A9. Three identical wheels move in different ways, as shown and described below:

Wheel A slides along a smooth surface at constant speed v. (The top view is shown.)

Wheel B rotates around a fixed axle with every point on its rim moving at speed v.

Wheel C rolls without slipping across the floor. Its center moves with speed v.

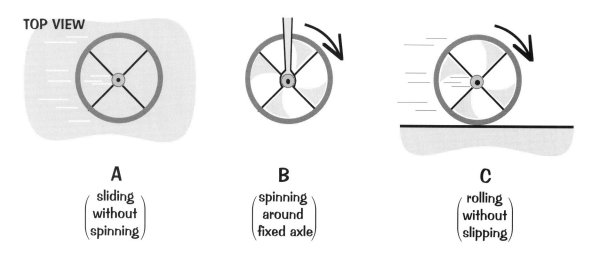

TOP VIEW

A
(sliding without spinning)

B
(spinning around fixed axle)

C
(rolling without slipping)

(a) Which wheel has the largest momentum? Which wheel has the smallest momentum? Explain.

(b) Which wheel has the largest kinetic energy? Which wheel has the smallest kinetic energy? Explain.

Integration of Ideas

Fill in the blanks in the following table listing the similarities and differences between kinetic energy and momentum.

	SIMILARITIES		DIFFERENCES
I1.	(a) Both momentum and kinetic energy depend upon the _____ and the _____ of the object.	(b)	Only the momentum depends on the _____ . The kinetic energy does not depend upon it.
I2.	(a) When both change, we know there must be a _____ exerted on the object.	(b)	_____ is a vector quantity, but _____ is a scalar quantity.
I3.	(a) For a collection of objects, both the <u>total</u> momentum and the <u>total</u> kinetic energy are found by _____ .	(b)	Whenever there is a net force on an object, its _____ <u>must</u> change, whereas in some cases its _____ does <u>not</u> change.

Reflection

R1. In general, which is more difficult to determine, the total momentum or the total kinetic energy? Explain.

R2. If you know the momentum of an object, can you determine its kinetic energy? If your answer is yes, explain how. If your answer is no, what additional information is needed?

R3. If you know the kinetic energy of an object, can you determine its momentum? If your answer is yes, explain how. If your answer is no, what additional information is needed?

R4. Is it possible to have a non-zero total momentum, but zero total kinetic energy? Explain. If your answer is yes, give an example.

R5. Is it possible to have a non-zero total kinetic energy, but zero total momentum? Explain. If your answer is yes, give an example.

R6. Give an example of a situation in which the momentum of an object changes, but the kinetic energy does not. Give an example of a situation in which the total kinetic energy changes but the total momentum does not.

R7. Consider situation A3, in which a car and a truck are traveling side-by-side along the highway. If the same constant force were applied to stop each vehicle, which would travel the longer displacement? Explain. Which would require more time to stop? Explain. (**Hint:** Draw sketches of velocity vs. time for the two vehicles. What do the slopes of these graphs represent? Which graph has the larger slope? Why? What do the areas below these graphs represent? Which graph has the larger area?)

Reasoning with Work and Energy Ideas

Purpose and Expected Outcome

The total work done on an object is equal to the change in its kinetic energy. This relationship is called the *Work–Kinetic Energy Theorem*. In this activity, you will learn how to use this theorem to analyze physical situations. This will help you later to know when *Conservation of Energy* may be used, and will also help you solve problems.

Prior Experience / Knowledge Needed

You should know the definitions of work and kinetic energy, and be able to apply them to physical situations.

The *Work–Kinetic Energy Theorem* relates the total work done on an object to the change in its kinetic energy. We define the total work to be the sum of the work done by all the forces, internal and external, exerted on an object:

$$W_{\text{total}} \equiv W_{\text{normal}} + W_{\text{spring}} + W_{\text{gravitation}} + \dots \qquad \textbf{definition of \underline{total} work}$$

This is equal to the change in the object's total kinetic energy:

$$W_{\text{total}} = \Delta E_{K,\text{total}} \qquad \textbf{Work–Kinetic Energy Theorem}$$

For a rigid, non-rotating object, the net force can be used to determine the total work, and the total mass can be used to find the initial and final kinetic energies. In this special case, we get:

$$F_{\text{net}}\, d \cos\theta = \Delta\left(\tfrac{1}{2} M v^2\right) \qquad \text{(for a rigid, non-rotating body of total mass } M\text{)}$$
$$= \tfrac{1}{2} M\left(v_f\right)^2 - \tfrac{1}{2} M\left(v_i\right)^2$$

For a <u>collection</u> of rigid, non-rotating objects, we add up the total work done on all the objects and set it equal to the change in the total kinetic energy. **Note:** When we studied momentum, internal forces were not as important as external forces, because internal forces deliver <u>no</u> net impulse to the system. Energy is different. Internal forces <u>can</u> do work on a collection of objects. This happens whenever the displacements of two interacting objects are different, such as when one object slides across another, or when two objects pull on each other via the gravitational force.

One consequence of the Work–Kinetic Energy Theorem is that when the <u>total</u> work done on a system is zero, the <u>total</u> kinetic energy of the system remains constant.

Explanation of Activity

You will be presented with a variety of situations, each followed by one or more questions for you to answer.

A1. A cart of mass m rolls frictionlessly with a constant velocity **v** as shown.

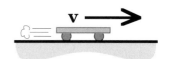

(a) How much work is needed to stop the cart? Explain

(b) How does this compare to the work needed to get the cart to change directions and move with a constant velocity of **−v**? Explain.

continued

A2. Consider the following two situations. In situation A, a ball rolls down an incline, while in situation B, a frictionless block slides down an identical incline. Their masses are the same, and they both start from rest at the same height.

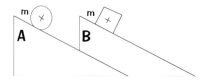

(a) In which case is the <u>kinetic energy</u> of the object larger when it reaches the bottom, or are they the same? Explain.

(b) In which case is the <u>momentum</u> of the object larger when it reaches the bottom of the incline, or are they the same? Explain.

A3. A cart moving with speed v collides with a spring firmly attached to a wall. When the cart loses contact with the spring again, it has reversed its direction.

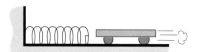

(a) What is the speed of the cart after losing contact with the spring? Use the Work–Kinetic Energy Theorem to explain your answer.

(b) How would the final speed of the cart change if friction were present? (Would it be larger than, smaller than, or the same as your answer to part (a)?) Explain.

A4. Two carts are released from rest as shown.

(a) As the two carts move away from each other, does their total kinetic energy change? What is the net force on the system? (Is it zero or non-zero?) Is the total work done on the two carts zero or non-zero? Explain your answers.

(b) As the two carts move away from each other, does their total momentum change? Is the net impulse delivered to the system zero or non-zero? Explain.

A5. A single force does work on an object. Its variation with position is shown in the graph to the right. Initially, the object is at the origin and moving in the positive direction.

(a) What is the object's position when its speed is largest?

(b) What is the object's position when its speed is the same as its initial speed?

(c) Can you determine where the object comes to rest? If so, where? If not, explain why not.

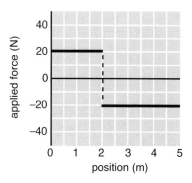

Reflection

R1. Can the momentum of an object change without any work being done on the object? Explain.

R2. Can the total kinetic energy of an object change without any impulse being delivered to the object? Explain.

R3. A cart with a spring bumper rolls along the floor toward a fixed wall. When the spring is maximally compressed, the cart is at rest. <u>While the cart is touching the wall</u>: Is work done on the cart to stop it? What forces do work on the cart to stop it? Do any external forces do work on the cart to stop it? Explain.

Solving Problems with the Work–Kinetic Energy Theorem

Purpose and Expected Outcome

Like the Impulse–Momentum Theorem, the Work–Kinetic Energy Theorem is a useful problem-solving principle. In this activity, you will learn how to apply the Work–Kinetic Energy Theorem to different situations. You will learn how to relate the forces exerted on an object to its displacement and changes in its speed.

Prior Experience / Knowledge Needed

You should know the definitions of work and kinetic energy, and be able to apply them to physical situations. You should be familiar with the Work–Kinetic Energy Theorem. Namely,

$$W_{\text{total}} = \Delta E_{K,\text{total}}$$ **Work–Kinetic Energy Theorem**

For a rigid, non-rotating object, we get:

$$W_{\text{total}} = \Delta\left(\tfrac{1}{2} M v^2\right) \qquad \text{(for a rigid, non-rotating body of total mass } M)$$
$$= \tfrac{1}{2} M\left(v_f\right)^2 - \tfrac{1}{2} M\left(v_i\right)^2$$

where W_{total} is the sum of the work done by <u>all</u> the forces exerted on the object.

Explanation of Activity and Example

For each of the problems below, first (a) indicate <u>how</u> you will use the definition of work, the definition of kinetic energy, and the Work–Kinetic Energy Theorem to solve for the desired unknown. Then (b) solve the problem and compute the value of the desired unknown. Use $g = 10\text{N/kg}$ throughout.

Example. A 600g ball rolls down a 1m ramp inclined at 30° as shown.

What is the kinetic energy of the ball when it reaches the bottom?

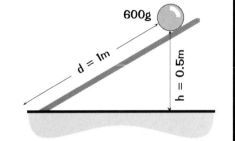

Answer:

The forces on the ball are (1) a normal force exerted by the incline, (2) a static friction force exerted by the incline, and (3) a gravitational force exerted by the earth. The work done by the normal force is zero, because it always points perpendicular to the displacement. The work done by the static friction force is zero, because the force is exerted through zero displacement. The work done by the gravitational force is positive and equal to the force of gravitation multiplied by the vertical component of the displacement. The total work is equal to the change in kinetic energy. We know the initial kinetic energy (zero), so we can find the final kinetic energy.

The solution is shown below. The Work–Kinetic Energy Theorem states:

$$W_{\text{total}} = \Delta E_{K,\text{total}}$$

Using the definitions of total work and change in kinetic energy, we get:

$$W_{\text{normal}} + W_{\text{static friction}} + W_{\text{gravitation}} = E_{K,f} - E_{K,i}$$

Using the definitions of work and kinetic energy, we get:

$$(0) + (0) + mgh = E_{K,f} - (0)$$

Inserting known values, we can solve for the final kinetic energy:

$$(0.6\text{kg}) \times (10\text{N/kg}) \times (0.5\text{m}) = E_{K,f}$$
$$3\text{J} = E_{K,f}$$

The kinetic energy of the ball when it reaches the bottom of the incline is 3J.

Note: *Different parts of the ball are moving at different speeds, so we <u>cannot</u> determine the speed of the ball when it reaches the bottom.*

A1. A child on a skateboard (total mass 50kg) is moving at 4m/s when she flies off a set of steps 1m high.

What is her speed just before she lands on the ground?

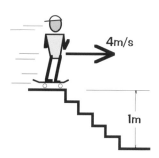

A2. A 1kg cart (A) rolls frictionlessly and collides with an identical cart (B) at rest. After the collision, the carts stick together and move off with a speed of 20cm/s.

What is the <u>maximum</u> amount of kinetic energy lost during the collision? (**Hint:** Find the initial speed of A.)

A3. A 0.4kg block is released from rest on a frictionless track as shown. In the middle of the track is a rough patch 70cm long.

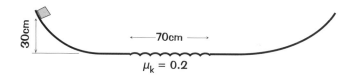

(a) What is the maximum speed of the block? Where does this occur?

(b) What is the final speed of the block? Where does this occur?

A4. A bungee jumper (mass 80kg) steps off the side of a bridge and falls a distance of 30m before stopping and springing back up again. A sketch of the force exerted by the bungee cord is provided at right. (The cord has a relaxed length of 10m.)

What is the maximum force exerted by the bungee cord on the bungee jumper?
(**Hint:** What is the total work done on the bungee jumper?)

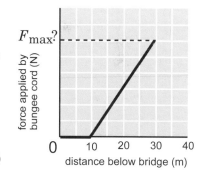

A5. A 100kg basketball player jumps 0.8m into the air to block a shot.

What is the smallest amount of work that the basketball player must do in order to block the shot?

A6. A 100kg basketball player jumps 0.8m into the air to block a shot.

Estimate the player's speed just after losing contact with the floor?

Reflection

R1. Which problems did you have difficulty solving? Do you know why these problems were difficult? Summarize and explain the difficulties you had.

R2. While solving these problems, did you ask yourself any of the following questions?

- What forces are exerted in this situation?
- What is the change in kinetic energy?
- Which forces do work?
- What is the total work done in this situation?
- Is each work done positive or negative?

If you did not, then you probably had difficulty solving these problems. Pick a problem you could not do before and try it again, keeping in mind these questions.

Recognizing the Presence of Potential Energy

Purpose and Expected Outcome

We have so far studied two related energy concepts: work and kinetic energy. When positive work is done, kinetic energy increases; when negative work is done, kinetic energy decreases. In this activity, we introduce the concept of *potential energy*. During this activity, you will develop an informal, gut-level sense of when a system has potential energy, and when the potential energy changes. After finishing this activity, you will be able to: (a) recognize the presence of potential energy, and (b) identify the interactions that are associated with potential energy.

Prior Experience / Knowledge Needed

You should know the definitions of work and kinetic energy, and be able to apply them to physical situations. You should be familiar with the Work–Kinetic Energy Theorem.

POTENTIAL ENERGY

You already know about one form of energy: kinetic energy—the energy associated with the motion of objects. There is another form of energy that is useful for understanding situations and solving problems: *potential energy*—the energy associated with the <u>relative positions</u> of two interacting objects.

Potential energy is more difficult to define than kinetic energy, but we can develop an intuitive sense using what we know about work and kinetic energy. Imagine picking up a book off the floor and slowly raising it 1 meter. You are doing work on the book, but the kinetic energy of the book does not change. This is because the <u>total</u> work done on the book is zero. The work you do on the book is done <u>against</u> the earth's gravitational force, which does an equal amount of negative work. The work done on the book is not "lost" because now you can drop the book and it will gain kinetic energy due to the work done by the earth's gravitational force. The amount of kinetic energy gained by the book is <u>exactly</u> equal to the amount of work done by the earth's gravitational force <u>and</u> exactly equal to the amount of work you did originally on the book!

So think of the situation like this: You pick up the book, increasing its <u>potential energy</u>. When you let go of the book, the book loses potential energy, but gains the same amount of kinetic energy. There are two ways to think about potential energy:

(1) If an interaction between two objects is capable of <u>increasing the kinetic energy</u> of the two objects as they move, then we associate a potential energy with that interaction.

(2) If an interaction between two objects is capable of <u>doing positive work</u>, then we also associate a potential energy with that interaction.

Note that potential energy is always associated with an interaction between two objects.

Explanation of Activity

For each of the situations described below, first (a) indicate whether or not you think potential energy is present in the situation; then, (b) identify the interactions you think are associated with any potential energy in the situation; and (c) explain your answers.

A1. Two carts are connected by a compressed spring. Consider the carts and the spring.

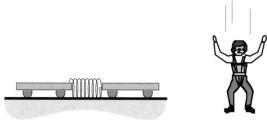

A2. A parachutist is falling toward the earth at terminal velocity. Consider the earth, the air, and the parachutist.

A3. A book slides across a table. Consider the book and the table.

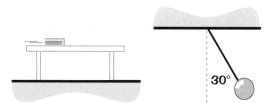

A4. A pendulum is made from a ball attached to a light piece of string. Consider the earth, the ball, and the string.

A5. Two blocks are connected by a light string passing over a pulley. Consider the two blocks, the pulley, the string, and the earth.

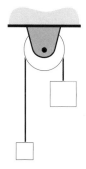

A6. A rubber ball collides with a wall. Consider the ball and the wall, while they are touching.

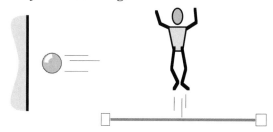

A7. A gymnast is jumping on a trampoline. Consider the earth, the trampoline, and the gymnast.

A8. A helium balloon is released into the air. Consider the air, the earth, and the balloon.

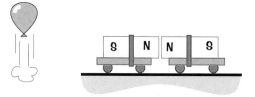

A9. Two magnets are attached securely to two carts as shown. Consider the two magnets and the two carts.

A10. A piston is used to increase the pressure inside a closed container of gas. Consider the container, the gas, and the piston.

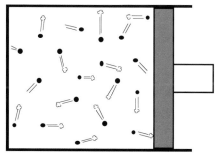

Reflection

R1. Of the following types of forces, which would you say can be associated with a potential energy? Explain.

❏ gravitation   ❏ spring force (and other elastic forces)   ❏ normal force

❏ tension force   ❏ force of air resistance   ❏ friction force

❏ magnetic force   ❏ buoyant force   ❏ electric force

R2. We stated earlier that potential energy is associated with an interaction between <u>two</u> objects. For each type of potential energy, give an example and identify the two objects (or pairs of objects) that are interacting to produce the potential energy. (For example, in the introduction, we used a book and the earth as the pair of objects producing gravitational potential energy between them.)

Comparing the Potential Energy

Purpose and Expected Outcome

In this activity, you will learn what physical characteristics affect the potential energy.

Prior Experience / Knowledge Needed

You should know the definition of work. You should be familiar with the concept of potential energy.

POTENTIAL ENERGY

Potential energy is produced by forces that can either (1) do <u>positive</u> work on, or (2) <u>increase</u> the kinetic energy of interacting objects. We will consider two basic types of interactions that produce potential energy: gravitational and elastic (springs, rubber bands, deformable balls, etc.).

To estimate the amount of potential energy present in a situation, imagine doing work against the given force. For example, to determine the amount of potential energy stored by gravitation when a ball is at a certain height above the earth, do this: Start with the ball on the ground. This will be our *reference point* for this case. Then slowly lift the ball to the desired height. The work you do in lifting the ball to that height is the potential energy (relative to the ground) possessed by the earth–ball system. In other words, the energy you use to lift the ball is stored in the gravitational attraction between the ball and the earth.

We use the same procedure using springs, with the relaxed spring as our reference. Whether we pull or push on the spring, we always do positive work on the spring to change its length. This means that the potential energy stored in a spring is always positive, while the gravitational potential energy can be negative if we go below our reference point.

Explanation of Activity

There are two parts in this activity. In the first part you will compare the gravitational potential energy present in different arrangements of objects. In the second part, you will compare the elastic potential energy present in different situations.

PART A: Comparing Gravitational Potential Energy

Below are 9 situations involving balls, labeled A through I. All the balls are the same mass, except C, which is 4 times the mass of the others. Answer all the questions using only the earth–ball system in each of these situations.

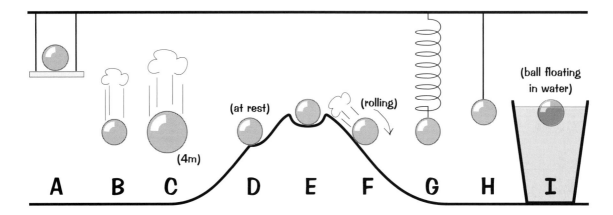

A1. Which situation(s) has (have) the largest gravitational potential energy?

A2. Which situation(s) has (have) the smallest gravitational potential energy?

A3. Which situation, A or B, has the larger gravitational potential energy, or are they the same? Explain.

A4. Which situation, B or C, has the larger gravitational potential energy, or are they the same? Explain.

A5. Which situation, A or C, has the larger gravitational potential energy, or are they the same? Explain.

A6. Which situation, D, E, or F, has the largest gravitational potential energy, or are two or more the same?

continued

A7. Which situation, G or H, has the larger gravitational potential energy, or are they the same?

A8. Which situation, H or I, has the larger gravitational potential energy, or are they the same?

Reflection for Part A

R1. Sort the following factors according to whether or not each <u>directly</u> affects the gravitational potential energy:

❏ size   ❏ shape   ❏ mass   ❏ speed
❏ velocity   ❏ horizontal position   ❏ density   ❏ vertical position
❏ color   ❏ reference height   ❏ elasticity   ❏ acceleration

R2. Did you use the <u>same</u> reference height for each ball in order to make your comparisons? If so, what height did you pick? If not, which answers would change if you used the same reference height throughout?

PART B: Comparing Elastic Potential Energy

Below are 9 situations involving springs, labeled A through I. All the springs are massless and identical, each having a relaxed length of L. The length of each spring is indicated. The masses of the blocks are proportional to their sizes. Answer all the questions using only these situations.

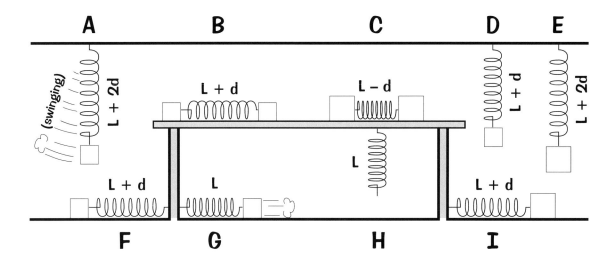

B1. Which situation(s) has (have) the largest elastic potential energy?

B2. Which situation(s) has (have) the smallest elastic potential energy?

B3. Which situation, B or C, has the larger elastic potential energy, or are they the same? Explain.

B4. Which situation, D or E, has the larger elastic potential energy, or are they the same? Explain.

B5. Which situation, A or E, has the larger elastic potential energy, or are they the same? Explain.

B6. Which situation, F or G, has the larger elastic potential energy, or are they the same?

B7. Which situation, G or H, has the larger elastic potential energy, or are they the same?

B8. Which situation, B, D, F, or I, has the largest elastic potential energy, or are two or more the same?

Reflection for Part B

R3. Which of the following factors <u>directly</u> affect the elastic potential energy?

❏ size of spring   ❏ mass of object attached to spring

❏ motion of spring   ❏ whether spring is compressed or stretched

❏ length of spring   ❏ length of spring relative to relaxed length

❏ mass of spring   ❏ temperature of surroundings

❏ spring constant   ❏ relaxed length of spring

❏ shape of spring   ❏ orientation of spring

R4. Did you use the <u>relaxed</u> length as the reference length for each spring in order to make your comparisons? If not, which answers would you change if you used the relaxed length instead?

R5. A spring is compressed a distance d. Is the potential energy positive or negative? A second spring is stretched a distance d. Is the potential energy positive or negative? Which spring has the larger elastic potential energy? Explain your answers.

Computing the Potential Energy

Purpose and Expected Outcome

You will learn how to compute the potential energy for gravitation and for ideal springs.

Prior Experience / Knowledge Needed

You should know the definitions of work and kinetic energy, and you should know the Work–Kinetic Energy Theorem. You should be familiar with the concept of potential energy. You should have some ideas about what factors affect the gravitational and the spring potential energies.

GRAVITATIONAL POTENTIAL ENERGY

With an object near the surface of the earth, the change in potential energy is the work done against the earth's gravitational force to change the height of the object. Mathematically, we write:

$$\Delta U_g \;=\; F_g \Delta y = mg\Delta y \qquad \text{(near the surface of the earth)}$$

where
$$m \;=\; \text{mass of the object}$$
$$g \;=\; \text{gravitational constant (about 10N/kg near the earth)}$$
$$\Delta y \;=\; \underline{\text{change}} \text{ in height of the object}$$

To find the potential energy, we must first define a *reference height*. This is not always the origin. It is the height at which U_g is assigned the value of zero. Any reference height may be chosen, but you must use the same one for the entire problem. You must decide what is the best choice for any particular situation. Often, we set U_g to be zero at height $y = 0$. With this choice for the reference height, the gravitational potential energy can be written:

$$U_g \;=\; mgy \qquad \text{(near the surface of the earth relative to chosen reference)}$$

Even though an ideal spring does not exert a constant force, it does exert a predictable force, depending on its spring constant and how far it is compressed or stretched from its relaxed condition. Unlike gravitation, springs have a well defined reference length: its relaxed length. When relaxed, the spring exerts no force, it can do no positive work, and it cannot increase the kinetic energy of anything. Therefore, when the spring is relaxed, we say the spring has zero potential energy.

By pulling or pushing on a relaxed spring, we do positive work on the spring, increasing its potential energy. The potential energy of an ideal spring is:

$$U_s = \tfrac{1}{2}kd^2 \qquad \text{(for an ideal spring having spring constant } k\text{)}$$

where d = distance the spring is stretched or compressed from its relaxed state.

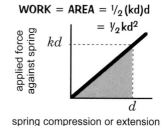

WORK = AREA = ½(kd)d
= ½kd²

applied force against spring

kd

d

spring compression or extension

(The factor of ½ is very important. It can be seen in the diagram to the right, because the work done on the spring is the area of the gray triangle.)

Sometimes it is more convenient to write the elastic potential energy in terms of the spring's actual length:

$$U_s = \tfrac{1}{2}k(L - L_0)^2 \qquad \text{(for an ideal spring having spring constant } k\text{)}$$

where L = length of the spring
L_0 = unstretched or "relaxed" length of the spring

In general, <u>you</u> must decide which form of U_s is best for the situation you are studying.

Explanation of Activity

In this activity, you will compute values for the potential energy and the change in potential energy for gravitation and for ideal springs in different situations. Diagrams of all the situations are shown below.

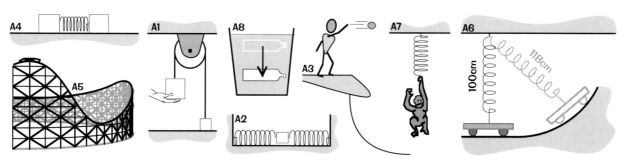

A1. A 2kg block and a 1kg block are attached to opposite ends of a string, and everything is placed on a pulley as shown. Initially, the 1kg block is on the ground and the 2kg block is 0.4m above the ground. After the 2kg block is released what is the change in potential energy of the system made up of the two blocks, the string, the pulley, and the earth.

A2. A 200g block is attached to two identical springs as shown. Initially, the springs are unstretched and are 20cm long. Each has a spring constant of 10N/cm. If the block is moved 10cm to the right, what is the total potential energy in the system?

A3. An 80kg person throws a 0.4kg ball off a small hill. The ball is released 1.5m above the top of the hill, and the hill is 2m high. Using the top of the hill as the reference height, what are...

(a) ... the potential energy of the earth–ball system immediately after it is released, and

(b) ... the potential energy of the earth–ball system when it hits the ground?

A4. A 30cm spring having k = 6N/cm is compressed to half its original length using two 1kg blocks as shown. What is the potential energy of the spring?

A5. A roller coaster car has a mass of 1000kg. During a test run the car travels empty from the topmost point to the end. The total distance traveled is 500m, and the total change in height is 75m. What is the change in potential energy of the system during this run?

A6. A 90cm spring with a spring constant of 0.1N/cm is securely attached to the ceiling. Its other end is attached to a 0.5kg cart, which is placed on a curved incline as shown. (The length of the spring is 118cm at this time.) The cart is released and eventually comes to rest as shown. (Its length is now 100cm.) What is the change in potential energy stored in the spring?

A7. A 40kg monkey hangs at rest from a spring having a spring constant of 25N/cm.

(a) What is the potential energy in the spring?

(b) Relative to the position of the monkey when the spring is unstretched, what is the gravitational potential energy of the earth–monkey system?

A8. An empty 1-liter bottle has a mass of about 80g. The sealed bottle is pushed into a bucket of water so that it is completely immersed as shown by the white outline in the diagram on the left. If the bottle is then pushed down 50cm farther into the water, what are the changes in the gravitational potential energy of...

(a) ... the empty bottle, and

(b) ... the water in the bucket?

Reflection

R1. Can the gravitational potential energy of a system be negative? If so, give an example. If not, explain why not.

R2. Can the potential energy of a spring be negative? If so, give an example. If not, explain why not.

R3. The gravitational potential energy of an object is negative, and it is released from rest. Is it possible for the kinetic energy of the object to increase? Give an example and show how this might happen. What happens to the gravitational potential energy?

Keeping Track of Energy: The Law of Conservation of Energy

Purpose and Expected Outcome

One of the most useful, pervasive, and powerful principles used in science is conservation of energy: In one form or another, the total amount of energy in the universe never changes. Even so, as the universe evolves, the amount of each <u>type</u> of energy changes, and the distribution of energy among the objects in the universe changes also.

If we focus on a single system, the energy of that system can change, but not without exchanging energy with another system. After finishing this activity, you will be able to (a) describe the different types of energy present in a system (i.e., kinetic, gravitational potential, etc.), (b) recognize when energy is being <u>converted</u> from one type to another (e.g., gravitational potential into kinetic energy), and (c) recognize when energy is being <u>transferred</u> from one system to another.

Prior Experience / Knowledge Needed

You should be thoroughly familiar with the concepts of *work*, *kinetic energy*, and *potential energy*, and you should know the Work–Kinetic Energy Theorem.

In all processes, energy is conserved. The only uncertainty is where the energy is located and what form it is in. So far, you have learned about two general forms of energy: *kinetic energy*, which is associated with the motion of objects, and *potential energy*, which is associated with the interactions between objects. A third type of energy is *mass energy*, which is associated with the mass of objects, and is summarized in the relation, $E_{mass} = mc^2$. All energy consists of combinations of these three types. However, it is often convenient to think of each of these types on two different scales: *microscopic* (atomic; very small scale) and *macroscopic* (everyday; large scale). In fact, increases in temperature are usually associated with increases in microscopic kinetic energy.

We define the *total energy* of a system to be:

$$E_{system} \equiv E_{K,macro} + U_{macro} + E_{mass} + E_{micro}$$

"The total energy of a system is the sum of the total
macroscopic kinetic energy, the total macroscopic
potential energy, the total mass energy and the total
microscopic energy of the objects in the system."

When no work is done on the system, then we can write:

$$\Delta E_{system} = 0$$

"When no work is done on a system, the change in total
energy of the system is zero."

or:

$$\Delta E_{K,macro} + \Delta U_{macro} + \Delta E_{mass} + \Delta E_{micro} = 0$$

"When no work is done on a system, the change in total
macroscopic kinetic energy plus the change in total
macroscopic potential energy plus the change in total
mass energy plus the change in total microscopic energy
of the system is zero."

Explanation of Activity and Examples

There are two parts to this activity.

PART A: Describing Changes in Energy

For the time period indicated for each system, (a) identify any interactions that change the way energy is distributed within the system, and (b) describe how the interaction is changing how the energy is distributed.

E1. A crumpled piece of paper is released from rest and falls through the air. Consider the situation from the instant the paper is released until it reaches terminal velocity.

Answers:

(a) *The gravitational force between the paper and the earth, as well as the force of air resistance, are changing how energy is distributed in the earth–paper–air system.*

(b) *The gravitational force decreases the potential energy of the earth–paper–air system and increases the kinetic energy of the paper. The force of air resistance <u>reduces</u> the rate at which the kinetic energy is increasing, and increases the microscopic energy of the paper and of the air hitting it.*

A1. A book is initially sitting at rest on a table top. It is given a brief push and then released. Consider the book from the beginning of the push until it comes to rest again.

A2. A bowling ball collides with a pin. Consider the ball and the pin during the time period starting just before the collision and ending just afterwards. (See diagram.)

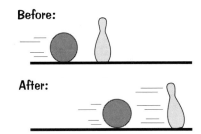

Before:

After:

A3. An amusement park bumper car crashes into a spring-backed barrier. Consider the car and the barrier from just before the car makes contact until the car stops.

A4. A spring is used to launch a marble off a table top. Consider the earth-spring-table-marble system from the time the marble is released until it is rolling on the floor at constant speed. (See diagram.)

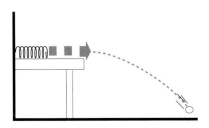

continued

A5. A gymnast is jumping up and down on a trampoline. Consider the earth-trampoline-gymnast system during one complete cycle:

      I.   in contact with the trampoline moving upward;

      II. in the air moving upward;

      III. in the air moving downward; and

      IV. in contact with the trampoline moving downward.

A6. A ping-pong ball is pushed into a bucket of water and released. The ball moves upward, eventually popping out of the water into the air. Consider the earth–water–ball system from the time the ball is released until the ball reaches its maximum height above the water.

A7. Two identical carts move toward each other at the same speed. The carts stick together and stop. Consider the two carts from the time when they are moving with constant speed until after they are stopped.

A8. A tray of ice is put into a warm oven. Consider the ice, the tray, the air, and the oven.

A9. A 5kg block is placed on a rough surface having a coefficient of sliding friction of 0.3. A string is attached to the block, which passes over a pulley and is attached to another block of unknown mass. If the 5kg block is given a tiny push, the system moves with constant speed.

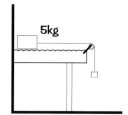

      I.   What is the mass of the hanging block?

      II. Describe how the energy in this situation changes while the hanging mass is falling.

PART B: Keeping Track of Energy

In this part, you are given different situations with partial information about the energy at different times. You should provide as much of the missing energy information as possible, based on your analysis of the system and the principle of conservation of energy. Use $g = 10$N/kg. You may assume that the changes in mass energy are always zero.

E2. A ball is dropped 50cm above ground level, and falls into a hole 20cm deep. Compare the energy of the system when the ball is dropped to the energy just before it hits the ground. Take the system to be the earth, the air, and the ball.

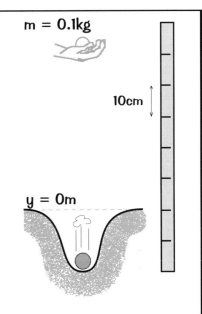

Answer: *There are three types of energy to consider: (1) gravitational potential energy U_g, (2) kinetic energy of the ball E_K, and (3) microscopic energy E_{micro}. Both U_g and E_K change by noticeable amounts. E_{micro} increases slightly (but negligibly compared to the other changes) due to air resistance (assuming the ball is much denser than air).*

The initial value of U_g is $(0.1kg)(10N/kg)(0.5m)$ $= 0.5J$, and its final value is $-0.2J$. The initial E_K is zero, and its final value can be determined using conservation of energy: Because the change in total energy must be zero, and neglecting the change in E_{micro}, the increase in kinetic energy must be equal to the decrease in potential energy: $E_{K,final} = 0.7J$.

Explanation: *Consider the bar graph at right showing the changes in each part of the total energy. The change in spring potential energy is zero. The change in microscopic energy is positive but very small. The change in gravitational potential energy is $-0.7J$ as shown at right, and the change in kinetic energy is just less than 0.7J. Note that the increases in energy are exactly matched by the decrease in gravitational potential energy. This is because the change in total energy must be zero.*

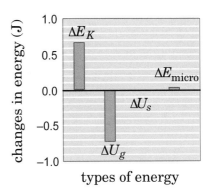

continued

B1. A spring is used to launch a ball into the air. (See diagram for all given information.) Take the system to be the earth, the spring, the air, and the ball. Use a bar graph to keep track of the changes in the different types of energy. (Be sure to label your axes.)

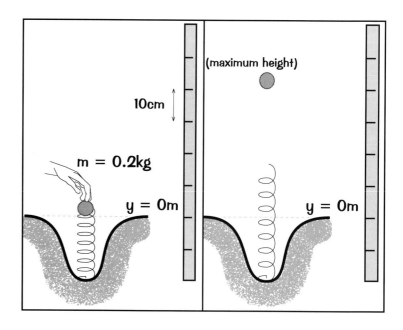

B2. A ball is dropped and bounces off the floor. (See diagram below for all necessary information.)

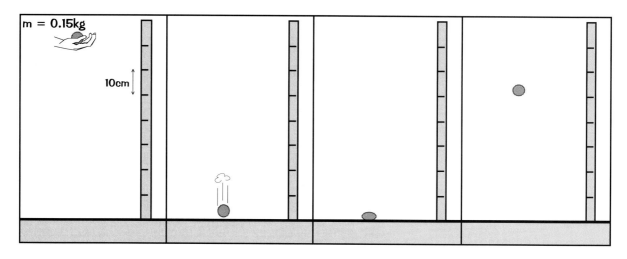

B3. A 1kg cart traveling at 20cm/s passes onto a piece of felt, ultimately coming to rest.

continued

Activity 92
Keeping Track of Energy: The Law of Conservation of Energy

B4. A bullet is embedded in a block of wood hanging from the ceiling as shown to the right. (See diagram.)

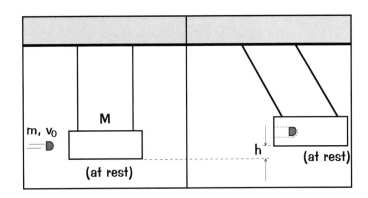

B5. An 80kg parachutist falls at a terminal velocity of 40m/s.

B6. A person jumps into the air from a crouched position. (Estimate all necessary quantities.)

B7. A block of wood is held down on a compressed spring as shown, and released. Soon afterwards the block rises to a height of 2cm above the uncompressed spring, and then falls back down again. After a very long time, the block comes to rest on the spring as shown at right.

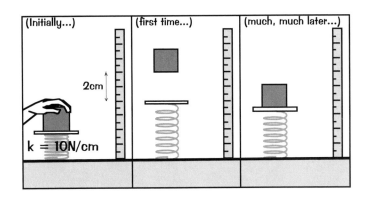

B8. A spring is held compressed and released from rest, rising into the air as shown below.

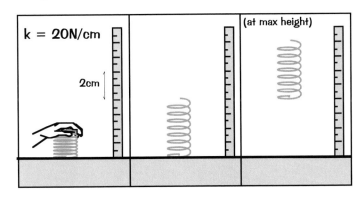

Reflection

R1. Can the spring potential energy ever be zero? If so, give an example. If not, explain why not.

R2. Can the kinetic energy of an object ever be zero? If so, give an example. If not, explain why not.

R3. Can the kinetic energy be negative? If so, give an example. If not, explain why not.

R4. Consider situation B8. Just before losing contact with the ground (middle frame), is the spring moving or at rest? Explain. Does the spring have a mass? If so, estimate its value. If not, explain why not.

R5. Consider the situation shown to the right. A block of mass m is pulled along a horizontal surface at constant speed using a rope.

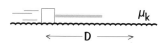

(a) How much work is done by the person pulling the rope in order to move the block a distance D? Where does this energy go?

(b) Derive an expression for the change in microscopic energy due to friction. Leave your answer in terms of μ_k, F_N, and D.

R6. Re-consider situation B5.

(a) How much work is done on the parachutist after falling a distance D? Where does this energy go?

(b) Derive an expression for the change in microscopic energy due to air resistance. Leave your answer in terms of A (the shape parameter), v (the speed) and D.

Reasoning with Energy Ideas

Purpose and Expected Outcome

You now have several major laws and principles with which to analyze problem situations. These include Newton's Laws of Motion, Conservation of Momentum, and Conservation of Energy. In this activity, you will learn how to use energy ideas to compare physical characteristics of different situations, and you will see how Conservation of Energy is different from the other physical principles you have learned so far. After finishing this activity, you should be able to use all the major principles to analyze a physical situation.

Prior Experience / Knowledge Needed

You should know the concepts of force, mass, acceleration, velocity, speed, momentum, impulse, work and all the different forms of energy, and you should know how they are inter-related. You should know how to use Newton's Laws, Conservation of Momentum, and the Work–Kinetic Energy Theorem to analyze physical situations. You should be familiar with Conservation of Energy.

Explanation of Activity

For each situation below, use one or more of the following to answer the questions: Newton's Laws, Conservation of Momentum, the Work–Kinetic Energy Theorem, and Conservation of Energy.

A1. Identical guns are used to fire identical bullets into identical wooden blocks attached to strings as shown. The string attached to block A is half as long as the string attached to block B.

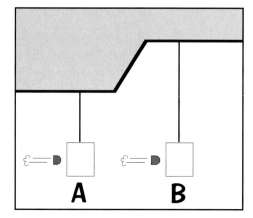

(a) Which block rises to the higher maximum height after the bullet becomes embedded in it? Explain.

(b) Which block reaches its maximum height first? Explain.

A2. During an explosion in mid-air, a piece of material splits into 2 pieces, one of which is twice the mass of the other. (You may assume that, during the explosion, external forces do no work and deliver no net impulse to the 2 pieces.)

(a) Which piece has the larger momentum? Explain.

(b) Which piece has the larger (macroscopic) kinetic energy? Explain.

(c) Which piece has the larger speed? Explain.

A3. Someone has made the following claim: "Under certain very special conditions, a heavy cart will reverse its velocity (same magnitude, opposite direction) after colliding with a lighter, initially stationary cart." Is this possible? Give an example, or explain why it is impossible. (You may assume that, during the collision, external forces deliver no net impulse and do no work.)

continued

A4. Two carts are used to compress a spring as shown. In one case, the two carts have the same mass of 5kg. In the second case, one cart has a mass of only 1kg, while the other has a mass of 9kg. Both springs are identical, both springs are compressed the same amount, and both systems are released from rest.

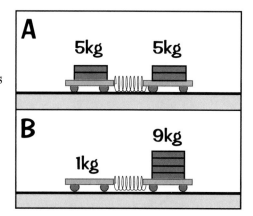

(a) Which cart (of the four) has the largest <u>kinetic energy</u> immediately after losing contact with the spring? Explain.

(b) Which cart (of the four) has the largest <u>momentum</u> immediately after losing contact with the spring? Explain.

(c) Long after being released, which pair of carts, A or B, is farthest apart? Explain.

A5. An inventor has created a spring-loaded toy that pops up off the table when compressed and released. The toy consists of two parts connected by a stiff spring as shown, with one of the parts being much heavier than the other. For which orientation, A or B, will the toy rise farther off the table after being compressed and released? Explain.

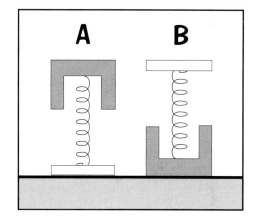

A6. Consider the pulley system shown at right. Four blocks (side A) are attached to one end of the string, and one block (side B) is attached to the other. The pulley also has mass. Consider the speed of the four blocks after falling a certain distance d.

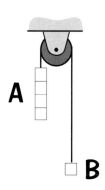

(a) Would the speed of the blocks be smaller, larger, or the same if the <u>mass of the pulley</u> was doubled, without changing its radius? Explain.

(b) Would the speed of the blocks be smaller, larger, or the same if the <u>mass of block B</u> was doubled, without changing anything else? Explain.

(c) Would the speed of the blocks be smaller, larger, or the same if the <u>mass of everything</u> was doubled, without changing any of the dimensions? Explain.

Reflection

R1. Of Newton's 2nd law, Conservation of Momentum, and Conservation of Energy, which would you say is the easiest to apply? Explain why you think so.

R2. For each of the following ideas, list the concepts, ideas, principles, and laws that you believe are <u>most closely</u> related to it.

   (a) mass

   (b) position

   (c) speed

   (d) velocity

   (e) acceleration

   (f) work

   (g) impulse

   (h) kinetic energy

   (i) force

   (j) potential energy

Solving Problems Using Energy Ideas

Purpose and Expected Outcome

In this activity, you will learn to apply energy principles to solve problems.

Prior Experience / Knowledge Needed

You should be thoroughly familiar with all of mechanics: position, displacement, velocity, and acceleration; forces and Newton's Laws; impulse, momentum, and Conservation of Momentum; and work, kinetic energy, potential energy, and Conservation of Energy.

WORK–ENERGY THEOREM

An alternative form for Conservation of Energy is derived for situations in which energy is exchanged between a system and its environment. It is called the Work–Energy Theorem, and it depends on the total work done by <u>external</u> forces and the change in <u>total</u> energy of the chosen system:

$$W_{\text{external}} = \Delta E_{\text{system}}$$ **Work–Energy Theorem**

When the work done by external forces is positive, energy is added to the system, so the total energy of the system increases. When the work done by external forces is negative, energy is removed from the system, so the total energy of the system decreases.

In many situations, this form of energy conservation is more convenient to apply. <u>You</u> must decide which form is best for the particular problem you are solving.

Explanation of Activity

Below are presented 7 problems. Before attempting a solution, you should think about and decide <u>how</u> you will solve each problem. In some cases, you are asked to provide various sketches. We strongly encourage you to consider sketches for all of the problems.

A1. A cannonball is shot at 50m/s from the edge of a cliff as shown. (The horizontal component of its velocity is 43m/s, and the vertical is 25m/s.) Estimate the speed of the cannonball just before it hits the ground.

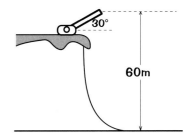

A2. An amusement park ride is being tested (see below). An empty car (mass 1000kg) is given an initial velocity at the beginning of the ride (A) as shown. Various other points along the track are labeled: Points C and E are both 40m above the lowest point B, and point D is 60m higher than B. The track ends at point F.

(a) Where is the speed of the empty car the largest?

(b) How fast is the empty car going at this time?

(c) Where is the speed of the empty car the smallest?

(d) How fast is the empty car going at this time?

(e) What is the final velocity of the car?

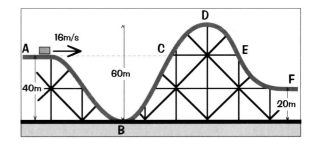

A3. A block is released from rest 6cm above a vertical spring as shown.

(a) Sketch the net force on the block vs. its height above the ground.

(b) Where is the speed of the block the largest? Explain.

(c) How fast is the block moving at this time?

(d) What is the maximum compression of the spring?

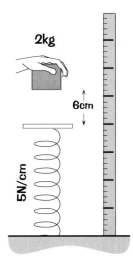

A4. A 10g bullet is shot at 160m/s into a 4kg block of wood as shown to the right. What is the maximum height achieved by the block after the bullet becomes embedded in it?

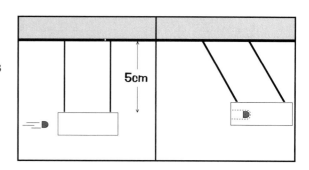

A5. A bungee jumper (mass 80kg) is attached to a 10m bungee cord attached to the top of a crane. For the first 5 meters of extension, the force exerted by the bungee cord increases by 2N for every 1cm that it is stretched (i.e., 200N/m). For any further extension, the force increases by only 1.2N for every 1cm that it is stretched (i.e., 120N/m).

(a) Sketch the elastic force vs. the length of the bungee cord.

(b) What is the maximum extension of the bungee cord in this situation?

A6. Two blocks are attached to opposite ends of a long string which passes over a massless pulley as shown. The system is released from rest.

(a) Assuming no friction between the 8kg block and the table, what is the speed of the 2kg block just before it hits the ground?

(b) Assuming a coefficient of kinetic friction of 0.2, what is the speed of the 2kg block just before it hits the ground?

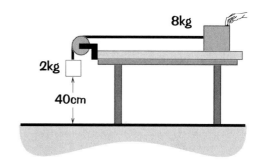

A7. A 0.4kg block is released from rest on a frictionless section of track as shown. In the middle of the track there is a rough patch 70cm long. <u>Exactly</u> where does the block come to rest?

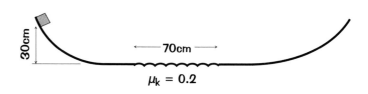

Reflection

R1. For which problems did you use Conservation of Momentum? Are there any other situations for which momentum is conserved? Which ones?

R2. For which problems could you use dynamics? Did you actually use dynamics in any of these? Which ones? What other methods are possible for solving these problems?

R3. For which problems did you use the Work–Kinetic Energy Theorem? What is it about these problems that makes the Work–Kinetic Energy Theorem particularly useful?

R4. For which problems did you use Conservation of Energy? What is it about these problems that makes the Conservation of Energy particularly useful?

R5. What are the similarities and differences between problem A3 and problem A5? How similar were your solutions to these problems?

R6. Derive an expression for the potential energy stored in the bungee cord of problem A5 when it has length L. (**Hint:** Your answer should depend on <u>both</u> slopes in your graph of force vs. length.)

Summarizing and Structuring Energy Ideas

Purpose and Expected Outcome

As you have already done for kinematics, interactions, dynamics, and momentum ideas, in this activity you will create a concept map showing the relative importance of and connections between energy ideas.

Prior Experience / Knowledge Needed

You should know the concepts associated with energy, and you should have some experience solving problems using energy ideas.

Explanation of Activity

There are 4 parts to this activity.

PART A: Summarizing Energy Concepts

Explain in your own words each of the following concepts and principles, and describe how they are related to each other and to other physical quantities (such as mass, position, velocity, speed, and force).

A1. Work

A2. Kinetic energy

A3. Work–Kinetic Energy Theorem

A4. Potential energy

A5. Microscopic energy

A6. Conservation of Energy

PART B: Comparing Summaries

Compare your statements with those of your classmates and rephrase them so that everyone agrees.

PART C: Creating a Concept Map

In a group or as a class, create a concept map of these ideas showing the relative importance of each, and showing the relationship of each to ideas covered previously in the course.

PART D: Adding More Problem-Solving Ideas

As a class, make any necessary additions to your sorted list of problem-solving ideas.

Recording Your Ideas
about Problem Solutions

Purpose and Expected Outcome

In this activity, you will learn about how you and your classmates categorize problems and their solutions. This will help you distinguish between problem-solving approaches.

Prior Experience / Knowledge Needed

You should have some experience solving physics problems.

Explanation of Activity

You will be shown 6 pairs of problems. You should <u>not</u> try to solve them. Just read carefully each pair of problems, decide whether or not they are solved using similar approaches. Then, give a reason for your decision.

A1. Consider the following two problems. Do you think they would be solved using similar approaches or different approaches? Explain your answer.

Problem A

A 10kg block is released from rest onto a curved frictionless track from an unknown height h. The block is traveling at 7m/s just before it collides and sticks to a 5kg block. From what height was the block released?

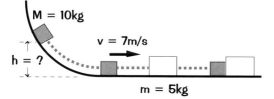

Problem B

A 10kg block is released from rest onto a curved frictionless track as shown. The block is traveling at 7m/s just before it collides and sticks to a 5kg block. What is the speed of the two blocks after the collision?

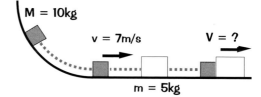

(continued on the next page)

A2. Consider the following two problems. Do you think they would be solved using similar approaches or different approaches? Explain your answer.

Problem A

A 10kg block is released from rest onto a curved frictionless track as shown. The block is traveling at 7m/s just before it collides and sticks to a 5kg block. What is the speed of the two blocks after the collision?

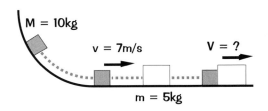

Problem B

A 60kg rollerblader pushes on an 80kg rollerblader with a force of 40N as shown. After the push the 60kg person is moving at 0.2m/s. How fast is the other person moving (if we ignore frictional effects)?

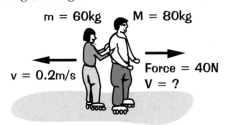

A3. Consider the following two problems. Do you think they would be solved using similar approaches or different approaches? Explain your answer.

Problem A

A 60kg rollerblader pushes on an 80kg rollerblader with a force of 40N as shown. After the push the 60kg person is moving at 0.2m/s. What is the acceleration of the other person during the push (if we ignore frictionaleffects)?

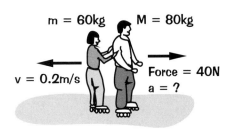

Problem B

A child on a skateboard is rolling down a ramp having straight and curved portions as shown. What is the acceleration of the skateboarder while on the straight portion (if we ignore the effects of friction and air resistance)?

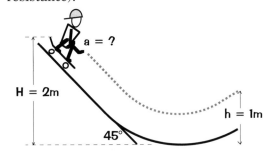

A4. Consider the following two problems. Do you think they would be solved using similar approaches or different approaches? Explain your answer.

Problem A

A child on a skateboard is rolling down a ramp having straight and curved portions as shown. What is the acceleration of the skateboarder while on the straight portion (if we ignore the effects of friction and air resistance)?

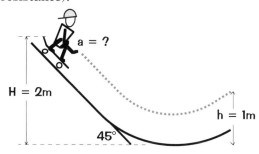

Problem B

A child on a skateboard is rolling down a ramp having straight and curved portions as shown. What is the speed of the skateboarder when she reaches the end of the ramp (if we ignore the effects of friction and air resistance)?

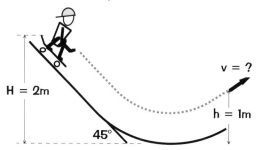

A5. Consider the following two problems. Do you think they would be solved using similar approaches or different approaches? Explain your answer.

Problem A

A 60kg rollerblader pushes on an 80kg rollerblader with a force of 40N as shown. After the push the 60kg person is moving at 0.2m/s. How fast is the other person moving (if we ignore frictional effects)?

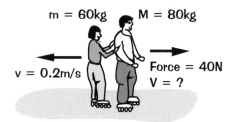

Problem B

A 60kg rollerblader pushes on an 80kg rollerblader with a force of 40N as shown. After the push the 60kg person is moving at 0.2m/s. What is the acceleration of the other person during the push (if we ignore frictionaleffects)?

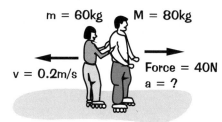

continued

A6. Consider the following two problems. Do you think they would be solved using similar approaches or different approaches? Explain your answer.

Problem A

A child on a skateboard is rolling down a ramp having straight and curved portions as shown. What is the speed of the skateboarder when she reaches the end of the ramp (if we ignore the effects of friction and air resistance)?

Problem B

A 10kg block is released from rest onto a curved frictionless track from an unknown height h. The block is traveling at 7m/s just before it collides and sticks to a 5kg block. From what height was the block released?

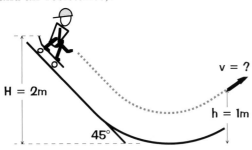

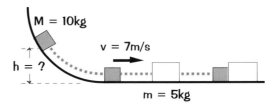

Reflection

R1. Re-examine the three pairs for which both problems used the same situation (pair #'s A1, A4, and A5). Did you say that the two problems were solved using the same approach or different approaches? If the same, did your reason involve characteristics of the physical situation, or something else? Explain.

R2. Re-examine the three pairs for which the problems used two different situations (pair #'s A2, A3, and A6). Did you say that the two problems were solved using the same approach or different approaches?

R3. For how many of the pairs did you use the physical situation to determine if they were solved using the same approach or different approaches? For how many pairs did you use physical concepts, principles, and laws to determine if they were solved using the same approach or different approaches?

Recognizing the Appropriate Principle/Law

Purpose and Expected Outcome

In this activity, you will learn how to recognize which physical principle or law is used to solve a problem most efficiently.

Prior Experience / Knowledge Needed

You should be thoroughly familiar with the central principles and laws of physics: Newton's Laws of Motion, the Impulse–Momentum Theorem, the Law of Conservation of Momentum, the Work–Kinetic Energy Theorem, and the Law of Conservation of Energy. You should have some experience solving problems. (It is recommended that you have done Activity 96, Recording your Ideas about Problem Solutions.)

DECIDING WHICH CONCEPT(S) CAN BE APPLIED TO SOLVE A PROBLEM

The main goal of physics is to describe nature accurately, and thereby predict physical phenomena. To do this, physicist look for the smallest number of "big ideas" that describe a wide range of physical situations. This allows someone to explain lots of things with only a few central ideas.

That is why principles and laws are so useful for solving problems. Although you will see a great number of problems in your physics course, they can all be solved by applying one or more of these central ideas. Once you decide which principles and laws apply to the problem, you can then choose a way of solving the problem, based on the given information and on the circumstances in the problem. This way of solving problems is more likely to be successful, because the equations you derive are more likely to be valid.

You have already seen that many problems are solved by applying physical principles and laws. Take for example Newton's second law. If you look back at Activities 65 and 66, you will see that this physical law appears near the beginning of every solution plan. In other words, deciding which principle or law applies to a problem is an important first step in solving the problem. Therefore, the ability to select appropriate principles and laws is a critical skill that you will need to be a successful problem solver.

Deciding which principles or laws apply to a problem is not easy. Sometimes two problems look similar, but depending on what you are asked to find, they might be solved in very different ways. On the other hand, two problems that look very different might actually be solved using the same principle or law.

For many problems, two different approaches are equally applicable. In these cases, you have the opportunity to choose from among the allowed solutions. Usually you would choose the method that is most efficient or easiest to apply. If you are unsure of your answer, you can use an alternate method to check your answer. As you become more experienced in problem solving, you will find it easier to base your solution on concepts first and equations second, rather than equations first and only.

Explanation of Activity and Examples

In this activity, you will examine the same problems you saw in Activity 96. Each problem can be solved using one of the following laws: (1) Newton's second law, (2) Conservation of Momentum, or (3) Conservation of Energy. Re-read each problem carefully, and decide which of these three laws would be used to solve the problem <u>most efficiently</u>. Then re-consider whether or not you think the two problems in each pair would be solved using similar approaches, <u>without solving the problems</u>. Finally, check to see whether or not your answer is the same as your answer in Activity 96.

E1. Consider the two problems described below.

Problem A

A 2kg wooden block is attached to one end of a spring, while the other end is pressed against a wall. The spring and the block rest on a frictionless, horizontal surface, and the spring has a negligibly small mass. If the spring is compressed until it exerts a force of 6N on the block, what is the initial acceleration of the block after it is released?

Problem B

A 2kg wooden block and a 1kg wooden block are used to compress a spring that is placed between them. (The spring is compressed but not attached to either block.) The system rests on a frictionless, horizontal surface, and the spring has a negligibly small mass. When the system is released from rest, the 2kg block is observed to move with a maximum speed of 0.5m/s. What is the maximum speed of the 1kg block?

$F_s = 6N$
$a = ?$
$M = 2kg$

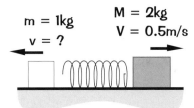

(a) Which principle would you use to solve problem A? Explain.

Answer: *Problem A is solved most efficiently using Newton's 2nd law.*

(b) Which principle would you use to solve problem B? Explain.

Answer: *Problem B is solved most efficiently using Conservation of Momentum.*

(c) Are these two approaches similar or different?

Answer: *These approaches are different.*

continued

E2. Consider the two problems described below.

Problem A

A 1000kg sports car is parked on a steep hill, when its emergency brake fails and it is observed to accelerate at 1m/s². What is the net force on the car?

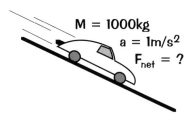

M = 1000kg
a = 1m/s²
F_{net} = ?

Problem B

A 2kg wooden block is attached to one end of a spring, while the other end is pressed against a wall. The spring and the block rest on a frictionless, horizontal surface, and the spring has a negligibly small mass. If the spring is compressed until it exerts a force of 6N on the block, what is the initial acceleration of the block after it is released?

F_s = 6N
a = ?

M = 2kg

(a) Which principle would you use to solve problem A? Explain.

Answer: *Problem A is solved most efficiently using Newton's 2nd law.*

(b) Which principle would you use to solve problem B? Explain.

Answer: *Problem B is solved most efficiently using Newton's 2nd law.*

(c) Are these two approaches similar or different?

Answer: *These approaches are similar.*

A1. Consider the two problems described below.

Problem A

A 10kg block is released from rest onto a curved frictionless track from an unknown height *h*. The block is traveling at 7m/s just before it collides and sticks to a 5kg block. From what height was the block released?

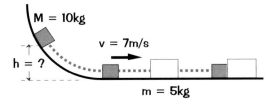

Problem B

A 10kg block is released from rest onto a curved frictionless track as shown. The block is traveling at 7m/s just before it collides and sticks to a 5kg block. What is the speed of the two blocks after the collision?

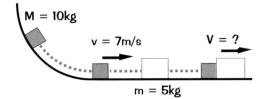

(a) Which principle would you use to solve problem A? Explain.

(b) Which principle would you use to solve problem B? Explain.

(c) Are these two approaches similar or different?

(d) Is your answer to (c) the same as or different from the one you gave in Activity 96?

A2. Consider the two problems described below.

Problem A

A 10kg block is released from rest onto a curved frictionless track as shown. The block is traveling at 7m/s just before it collides and sticks to a 5kg block. What is the speed of the two blocks after the collision?

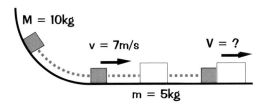

Problem B

A 60kg rollerblader pushes on an 80kg rollerblader with a force of 40N as shown. After the push the 60kg person is moving at 0.2m/s. How fast is the other person moving (if we ignore frictional effects)?

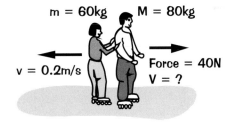

(a) Which principle would you use to solve problem A? Explain.

(b) Which principle would you use to solve problem B? Explain.

(c) Are these two approaches similar or different?

(d) Is your answer to (c) the same as or different from the one you gave in Activity 96?

continued

A3. Consider the two problems described below.

Problem A

A 60kg rollerblader pushes on an 80kg rollerblader with a force of 40N as shown. After the push the 60kg person is moving at 0.2m/s. What is the acceleration of the other person during the push (if we ignore frictionaleffects)?

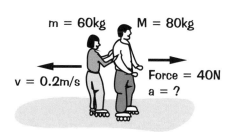

Problem B

A child on a skateboard is rolling down a ramp having straight and curved portions as shown. What is the acceleration of the skateboarder while on the straight portion (if we ignore the effects of friction and air resistance)?

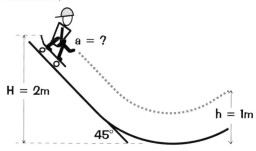

(a) Which principle would you use to solve problem A? Explain.

(b) Which principle would you use to solve problem B? Explain.

(c) Are these two approaches similar or different?

(d) Is your answer to (c) the same as or different from the one you gave in Activity 96?

A4. Consider the two problems described below.

Problem A

A child on a skateboard is rolling down a ramp having straight and curved portions as shown. What is the acceleration of the skateboarder while on the straight portion (if we ignore the effects of friction and air resistance)?

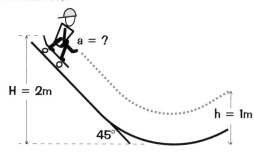

Problem B

A child on a skateboard is rolling down a ramp having straight and curved portions as shown. What is the speed of the skateboarder when she reaches the end of the ramp (if we ignore the effects of friction and air resistance)?

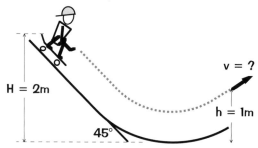

(a) Which principle would you use to solve problem A? Explain.

(b) Which principle would you use to solve problem B? Explain.

(c) Are these two approaches similar or different?

(d) Is your answer to (c) the same as or different from the one you gave in Activity 96?

A5. Consider the two problems described below.

Problem A

A 60kg rollerblader pushes on an 80kg rollerblader with a force of 40N as shown. After the push the 60kg person is moving at 0.2m/s. How fast is the other person moving (if we ignore frictional effects)?

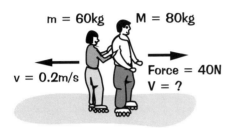

Problem B

A 60kg rollerblader pushes on an 80kg rollerblader with a force of 40N as shown. After the push the 60kg person is moving at 0.2m/s. What is the acceleration of the other person during the push (if we ignore frictionaleffects)?

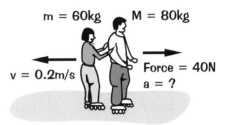

(a) Which principle would you use to solve problem A? Explain.

(b) Which principle would you use to solve problem B? Explain.

(c) Are these two approaches similar or different?

(d) Is your answer to (c) the same as or different from the one you gave in Activity 96?

A6. Consider the two problems described below.

Problem A

A child on a skateboard is rolling down a ramp having straight and curved portions as shown. What is the speed of the skateboarder when she reaches the end of the ramp (if we ignore the effects of friction and air resistance)?

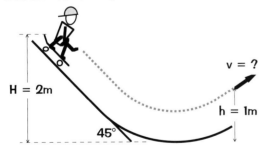

Problem B

A 10kg block is released from rest onto a curved frictionless track from an unknown height h. The block is traveling at 7m/s just before it collides and sticks to a 5kg block. From what height was the block released?

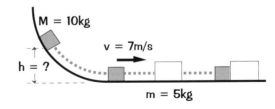

(a) Which principle would you use to solve problem A? Explain.

(b) Which principle would you use to solve problem B? Explain.

(c) Are these two approaches similar or different?

(d) Is your answer to (c) the same as or different from the one you gave in Activity 96?

Reflection

R1. What features of a problem suggest to you that Conservation of Energy should be used to solve it? Explain.

R2. What features of a problem suggest to you that Conservation of Momentum should be used to solve it? Explain.

R3. What features of a problem suggest to you that Newton's second law should be used to solve it? Explain.

R4. If you are given a problem that can be solved using either Newton's laws or the Impulse–Momentum Theorem, which would you choose to actually solve it? Explain.

R5. If you are given a problem that can be solved using either Newton's laws or the Work–Kinetic Energy Theorem, which would you choose to actually solve it? Explain.

R6. Give an example of a problem that is solved using Conservation of Momentum. Now use the <u>same</u> situation to create a problem that is solved using Conservation of Energy.

Matching Solution Strategies with Problems

Purpose and Expected Outcome

In this activity, you will learn what a *solution strategy* is, and how it is related to a problem's solution. After completing this activity, you should have a greater ability to recognize the situations and problems for which a certain principle or law is valid, and the conditions under which the principle or law can be applied properly.

Prior Experience / Knowledge Needed

You should be familiar with Newton's laws, Conservation of Momentum, Conservation of Energy, and how each applies to problems.

SOLUTION STRATEGIES

A *solution strategy* is a brief summary of the elements needed to solve a problem. It contains: (1) the principle (or law) that will be applied, (2) a brief justification explaining why the chosen principle is valid for the situation given in the problem and why the principle was chosen for <u>the particular</u> problem, and (3) an outline of the procedure that will be used to find the desired unknown. You can think of a solution strategy as the *What*, the *Why*, and the *How* of a problem's solution: *What* principle are you going to use? *Why* are you going to use it? *How* are you going to use it?

Why bother with a solution strategy? It draws your attention to the features of a problem that will help you solve it. Part (1) of the solution strategy focuses your attention on the concepts you will use to solve the problem. Part (2) helps you check to make sure that the chosen principle is valid and appropriate for the situation described in the problem. Part (3) helps you check to make sure you have enough given information to actually solve for the desired unknown.

Explanation of Activity

Below are six solution strategies followed by six problems. Match each problem with a solution strategy. Each solution strategy should be matched to only one problem.

SOLUTION STRATEGIES

Conservation of Energy A

Conservation of Energy can be applied to solve this problem, because the only *non-conservative* forces (friction and air resistance) are small enough to be ignored. To apply conservation of energy to this problem, set the initial energy (i.e., the sum of kinetic and potential energies) equal to the final energy. Initially the object's energy consists only of gravitational potential energy, and involves only one unknown. In the final state, the energy is purely kinetic, and all necessary quantities are known. There is only one unknown in our equation, which allows us to solve for the desired quantity.

Conservation of Momentum A

Conservation of Momentum can be applied to solve this problem, because the net impulse delivered by external forces (friction and air resistance) is small enough to be ignored. To apply conservation of momentum, set the initial momentum equal to the final momentum. The initial momentum is zero. Of the quantities needed to determine the final momentum, only the desired quantity is unknown. There is only one unknown in our equation, which allows us to solve for the desired quantity.

Newton's Laws A

Newton's 2nd law can be applied to solve this problem, because Newton's 2nd law relates the forces exerted on an object to its acceleration. We apply Newton's 2nd law by setting the net force on the object equal to its mass times its acceleration. There are two unknown quantities in this equation. One of these unknowns can be found by drawing a free-body diagram and determining the net force on the object. This leaves only one unknown, so we can solve our equation for the desired quantity.

Conservation of Energy B

Conservation of Energy can be applied to solve this problem, because the only *non-conservative* forces (friction and air resistance) are small enough to be ignored. To apply conservation of energy, set the initial energy equal to the final energy. Initially the object's energy consists only of kinetic energy, and all quantities needed to calculate it are known. In the final state, the energy is a combination of kinetic and gravitational potential energy. Of the quantities needed to calculate the final energy, only the desired quantity is unknown. There is only one unknown in our equation, which allows us to solve for the desired quantity.

Conservation of Momentum B

Conservation of Momentum can be applied to solve this problem, because the net impulse delivered by external forces (friction and air resistance) is small enough to be ignored. To apply conservation of momentum, set the initial momentum equal to the final momentum. The initial momentum can be found using given information. Of the quantities needed to determine the final momentum, only one is unknown. Solve for the unknown, then use it to calculate the desired quantity.

Newton's Laws B

Newton's 2nd law can be applied to solve this problem, because Newton's 2nd law relates the forces exerted on an object to its acceleration. We know the acceleration is zero, so the net force must be zero also. There are three forces exerted on the object, of which two are not known. By drawing a free-body diagram and determining the net force along a certain direction, we can solve for the desired quantity.

A1. A 10kg block is released from rest onto a curved frictionless track from an unknown height h. The block is traveling at 7m/s just before it collides and sticks to a 5kg block. From what height was the block released?

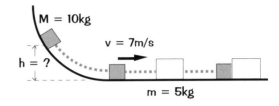

A2. A 60kg rollerblader pushes on an 80kg rollerblader with a force of 40N as shown. After the push the 60kg person is moving at 0.2m/s. How fast is the other person moving after the push (if we ignore frictional effects)?

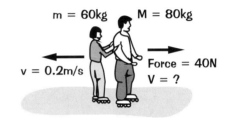

A3. A 1000kg car is at rest on a 25° hill. The coefficient of static friction between the rubber wheels and the road is 0.65. What is the magnitude of the friction force exerted on the car?

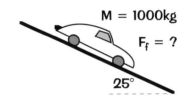

A4. A 60kg rollerblader pushes on an 80kg rollerblader with a force of 40N as shown. After the push the 60kg person is moving at 0.2m/s. What is the acceleration of the other person during the push (if we ignore frictional effects)?

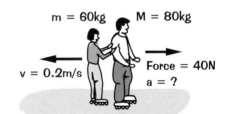

A5. A 100g toy car is traveling at 500cm/s along a track having a circular loop of radius 40cm. Ignoring the effects of air resistance and friction, what would be the speed of the car when it is at the topmost part of the track?

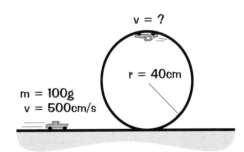

A6. A 4kg block is moving at 1m/s on a horizontal air table. (The air table is used to make the friction force very, very small.) The block eventually collides with a 2kg block. If the two blocks stick together after the collision, what is the kinetic energy of the two blocks just after they collide?

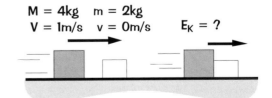

Integration of Ideas

For each of the problems, list (a) the principle that should be used to solve the problem. Then, list (b) the features of the situation and (c) the given information that were <u>relevant</u> to deciding which principle should be used. Finally, list (d) the features and (e) the given information that were <u>not</u> relevant to deciding the appropriate principle. (Examples have been provided for each category, but you should add to these lists.)

	(a) Principle	(b) Relevant Features	(c) Relevant Givens	(d) Irrelevant Features	(e) Irrelevant Givens
I1.					• mass of second block
I2.		• no net impulse delivered by external forces		• people facing the same direction	
I3.			• mass of car		
I4.		• mass of heavier person (man) is known			• final velocity of lighter person (girl)
I5.			• initial speed of car		
I6.			• looking for final kinetic energy		

Reflection

R1. Re-consider problem A1. If the track had a coefficient of friction of 0.2, would you be able to solve the problem? Why or why not? Could the Work–Kinetic Energy Theorem be used to solve it? Explain.

R2. Re-consider problem A3. If the coefficient of static friction had <u>not</u> been given, would you still be able to solve the problem? Why or why not?

R3. Create a problem in which <u>both</u> Conservation of Energy and Conservation of Momentum are needed to solve it.

Writing and Comparing Solution Strategies

Purpose and Expected Outcome

In this activity, you will learn more about how to recognize the appropriate principle needed to solve a problem, and how this choice relates to the features of the problem.

Prior Experience / Knowledge Needed

You should have some experience with *solution strategies*.

SOLUTION STRATEGIES

A *solution strategy* is a brief summary of the elements needed to solve a problem. It contains: (1) the principle (or law) that will be applied, (2) a brief justification explaining why the chosen principle is valid for the situation given in the problem and why the principle was chosen for <u>the particular</u> problem, and (3) an outline of the procedure that will be used to find the desired unknown. You can think of a solution strategy as the *What*, the *Why*, and the *How* of a problem's solution: *What* principle are you going to use? *Why* are you going to use it? *How* are you going to use it?

Why bother with a solution strategy? It draws your attention to the features of a problem that will help you solve it. Part (1) of the solution strategy focuses your attention on the concepts you will use to solve the problem. Part (2) helps you check to make sure the chosen principle is valid and appropriate for the situation described in the problem. Part (3) helps you check to make sure you have enough given information to actually solve for the desired unknown.

Explanation of Activity

You will be given 3 pairs of problems. You should <u>not</u> try to solve any of them. First write a complete solution strategy for problem A. Then read problem B and describe <u>what would be different</u> about the solution strategy for problem B. (You do <u>not</u> need to write a solution strategy for problem B.)

A1. Consider the following two problems.

Problem A

A 10kg block is released from rest onto a curved frictionless track as shown. The block is traveling at 7m/s just before it collides and sticks to a 5kg block. What is the speed of the two blocks after the collision?

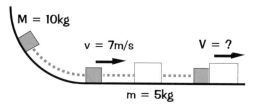

Problem B

A 2kg block slides frictionlessly at 3m/s toward another 2kg block at rest. After the collision, the first block remains at rest, and the second block travels frictionlessly at 2m/s until it reaches a 35° ramp as shown. How far up the ramp will the block slide?

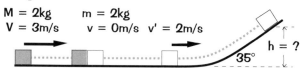

(a) Write a solution strategy for problem A. (Make sure to include the principle, a justification, and a procedure.)

(b) What would be different about a solution strategy for problem B? Explain.

A2. Consider the following two problems.

Problem A

A child on a skateboard is rolling down a ramp having straight and curved portions as shown. What is the acceleration of the skateboarder while on the straight portion (if we ignore the effects of friction and air resistance)?

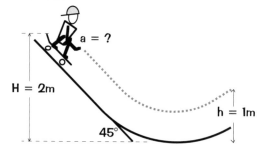

Problem B

A 1000kg sports car is attempting to stop at the bottom of a steep 30° hill. If the maximum rate possible under these conditions is 1m/s², what is the force of friction on the car while it is stopping? (Ignore air resistance.)

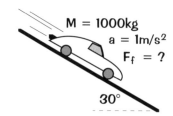

(a) Write a solution strategy for problem A.

(b) What would be different about a solution strategy for problem B? Explain.

A3. Consider the following two problems.

Problem A

A child on a skateboard is rolling down a ramp having straight and curved portions as shown. What is the speed of the skateboarder when she reaches the end of the ramp (if we ignore the effects of friction and air resistance)?

Problem B

A 0.2kg brass ball is attached to one end of a 1.5m string, whose other end is firmly attached to the ceiling. The ball is initially held with the string perfectly horizontal, and released from rest. What is its speed at the bottom when the string is perfectly vertical?

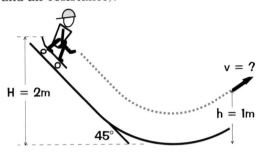

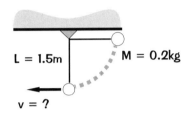

(a) Write a solution strategy for problem A.

(b) What would be different about a solution strategy for problem B? Explain.

Reflection

R1. Make a list of the physics principles used to write the solution strategies in this activity. What principles are missing from this list that might be used to solve problems?

R2. The Law of Conservation of Energy states that no amount of energy can be created or destroyed; the total amount of energy in the universe always remains the same. Under what conditions is it <u>not</u> possible to use this principle to solve a problem or determine an unknown quantity? Give at least two examples of situations for which energy is conserved but not in a way that is useful for determining an unknown quantity.

R3. Newton's second law ($\mathbf{F}_{net} = m\mathbf{a}$) is always true. Under what conditions is it <u>not</u> possible to use Newton's second law to solve a problem or determine an unknown quantity? Give at least two examples of situations for which Newton's second law is not useful for determining an unknown quantity.

Solving One-Principle Problems

Purpose and Expected Outcome

In this activity, you will learn how to apply principles to problems.

Prior Experience / Knowledge Needed

You should be familiar with solution strategies. In particular, you should know the definition and purpose of each part of a solution strategy: (1) the principle, (2) the justification, and (3) the procedure.

Explanation of Activity

In this activity, you will solve 6 problems, each of which requires only one principle to solve. We encourage you to think about <u>what</u> principle you should apply, <u>why</u> it can be validly applied, and <u>how</u> you will apply it before solving each problem.

A1. A 10kg block is released from rest onto a curved frictionless track from an unknown height h. The block is traveling at 7m/s just before it collides and sticks to a 5kg block. From what height was the block released?

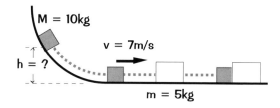

A2. A 1000kg car is at rest on a 25° hill. The coefficient of static friction between the rubber wheels and the road is 0.65. What is the magnitude of the friction force exerted on the car?

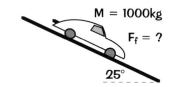

A3. A 200g wooden block is released from rest from a height of 40cm above a rough, horizontal surface as shown. Assuming the block slides frictionlessly until it reaches the rough patch, how far into the rough patch will the block go before stopping?

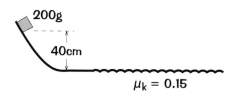

A4. A 5000kg motorboat is traveling at 3m/s on a calm river. To pass another boat, the captain increases the throttle, resulting in the motorboat experiencing the net force shown to the right. What is the speed of the motorboat at $t = 60$s?

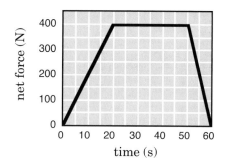

continued

A5. A 0.2kg brass ball is attached to one end of a 1.5m string, whose other end is firmly attached to the ceiling. The ball is initially held with the string perfectly horizontal, and released from rest. What is its speed at the bottom when the string is perfectly vertical?

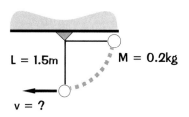

A6. A 2kg wooden block and a 1kg wooden block are used to compress a spring that is placed between them. (The spring is compressed but not attached to either block.) The system rests on a frictionless, horizontal surface, and the spring has a negligibly small mass. When the system is released from rest, the 2kg block is observed to move with a maximum speed of 0.5m/s. What is the maximum speed of the 1kg block?

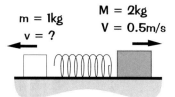

Reflection

R1. Re-consider problem A1. Is there enough given information to determine the speed of the two blocks after they collide and stick together? If so, what principle would you use to determine it? If not, explain why not.

R2. Re-consider problem A3. Did you calculate a value for the speed of the block just before it entered the rough region? If so, explain how you might find the desired quantity without determining this speed. If not, check your answer with someone else and resolve any differences.

R3. Re-consider problem A6. Is there enough information to determine the energy stored in the spring before the blocks are released? If so, what principle would you use to determine it? If not, explain why not.

R4. Did you use <u>exactly</u> one principle to solve each problem? If not, which problems required more than one principle? For each problem, compare your solutions with other students and determine which <u>single</u> principle was probably "best" for that problem.

Solving More Complex Problems

Purpose and Expected Outcome

Not all problems require exactly one principle to solve. Some require two or even three to solve. Other problems require a more careful analysis of the concepts involved than most. In this activity, you will learn how to apply concepts and principles more thoroughly to different types of problems.

Prior Experience / Knowledge Needed

You should be familiar with all the concepts, principles, and operations needed to solve problems in mechanics. You should know how to determine which principles apply to a problem situation, and how to choose the most appropriate principle.

There are a number of ways that a problem can be made complex. Before solving some of them, it might help you to see some of the different types.

Sequential many-principle problems. Perhaps the simplest type of complex problem is one in which the process described can be broken down into a number of one-principle problems. The key to solving this type is recognizing each of the sub-processes going on within the problem. Consider the following problem:

> A 10kg block slides frictionlessly from a height of 20cm, starting from rest. It collides and sticks to a 5kg block. What is the speed of the pair after the collision?
>
>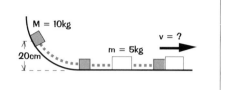

This problem is really two problems put together. The collision at the end of the process conserves momentum, but we cannot determine the final speed without knowing the speed of the 10kg block before the collision. This is found by applying Conservation of Energy using the height from which it was released. <u>Then</u> we can use Conservation of Momentum to find the desired quantity.

Simultaneous many-principle problems. In this type, two or more principles must be applied at the same time. For instance, when a spring is used in a collision or in an "explosion", both energy and momentum are usually conserved during the interaction, and often, <u>both</u> must be applied to solve for the desired unknown.

Given information not suggestive of relevant concepts. What if you were given a graph of acceleration vs. position? How would you interpret it? How would you use it to analyze the situation? What principle is suggested by this graph? You probably have not ever seen a graph like this, but what happens if you multiply the acceleration by the mass of the object? This is the net force exerted on the object! And a graph of net force vs. position is often used to find the total work done an object. Therefore, even though the given information is highly suggestive of kinematics, in fact, the more relevant concepts might involve dynamics and energy instead.

Desired unknown not suggestive of relevant concepts. Re-consider the problem above. What if the question asked for the kinetic energy of the pair after sticking together? This is suggestive of energy concepts as being most relevant, but momentum conservation is needed to solve it. You must determine the final speed of the pair first, then apply the definition of kinetic energy to answer the question.

In general, try not to be misled by what is given or what is asked for, focus on the principles that can be applied, and try to break down the problem as much as possible before solving it.

Explanation of Activity

In this activity, you will solve 6 problems. We encourage you to think about <u>what</u> principles apply, <u>why</u> they can be validly applied, and <u>how</u> you will apply them before solving each problem.

A1. Two wooden blocks are used to compress a spring by 3cm. Neither block is attached to the spring, and both are released from rest. What are their speeds just after losing contact with the spring?

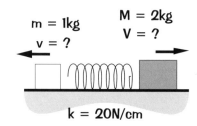

A2. A 1000kg sports car is attempting to stop at the bottom of a steep 30° hill. If the maximum rate possible under these conditions is 1m/s², what is the force of friction on the car while it is stopping? (Ignore air resistance.)

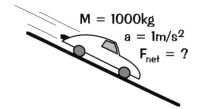

A3. A 5g bullet is shot at 120m/s into a 1kg block as shown. Estimate how far the block slides before stopping.

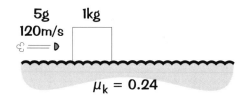

continued

A4. A slingshot is made by attaching 2 identical 5cm springs to two posts separated by 20cm as shown. A 50g metal ball is placed between the two springs and stretched until <u>each spring</u> is 20cm long. If the ball is released from rest, estimate its maximum speed.

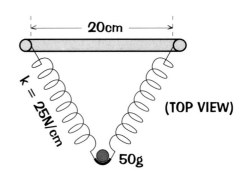

(TOP VIEW)

A5. A 20,000kg rocket is drifting in space at 80m/s as shown. At some point, the engines are fired to produce a force of 120,000N for 10s. What is the speed of the rocket at the end of the 10s time period?

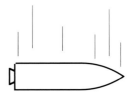

A6. A 20kg cannon ball is shot at 40m/s at an angle of 75°. At the top of its trajectory it explodes into two pieces, one of which falls straight to the ground. The other is observed to travel horizontally at 50m/s just after the explosion. What are the masses of the two fragments?

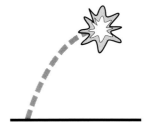

Structuring Mechanics

Purpose and Expected Outcome

Now that you have finished learning all the concepts associated with motion, interactions, Newton's laws, dynamics, and the conservation laws, it is time to organize them. This will make it easier to use all these ideas later to understand a situation better or to solve a problem. In this activity, you will arrange the concepts *hierarchically* according to which ideas are most useful for problem solving.

Prior Experience / Knowledge Needed

You should know all the major concepts associated with motion and how they are related to each other. You should be able to recognize common interactions and know the physical characteristics that govern the magnitude and direction of each. You should know Newton's laws and how they are used to understand physical situations. You should know how to use free-body diagrams, how to find the components of vectors, and how to break up vector equations into components. You should know how all these ideas are used in dynamics. You should know the major concepts involved with the conservation laws and know how they are related to each other. Finally, you should know the conservation laws and the circumstances in which they are valid.

Explanation of Activity

PART A: Prioritizing Concepts in Mechanics

A1. Create a list of concepts that are used for solving problems in mechanics. For each item in your list, rate it according to how useful and important it is for solving problems. (Use a scale of 1 to 10, with 1 for the most useful and important, and 10 for the least useful and important concepts in your list.) There should be between 4 and 8 items that are rated "most useful and important".

A2. Consider the topmost items in your list. Explain why each of these is particularly important and useful for problem solving.

A3. As a class, combine all the lists into a single list, and give each item a rating of 1 to 10, as before.

PART B: Arranging Concepts in Mechanics

Using the class-wide list generated in part A, arrange the items *hierarchically*, which means that they should be arranged with the most important concepts at the top, and less important items below them. Connect the items into a concept map to show how all these ideas are related.

Reflection

R1. Was there general agreement among you and your classmates about which ideas were useful for problem solving and which ideas were not so useful? Explain why or why not.

R2. Was your own way of thinking about mechanics affected by this activity? How? Do you think a hierarchical structure will help you decide how to solve a problem before solving it? Explain.

Reader

Chapter 3:
   CONSERVATION LAWS

— & —

Chapter 4:
   CONCEPT-BASED
   PROBLEM SOLVING

CONSERVATION LAWS

Introduction. A *conservation law* is a statement that, during a specific time interval and under certain conditions, "something" stays the same. In this chapter, we will study two conservation laws, one for *momentum* and one for *energy*. We will find that each of these conservation laws is very useful for analyzing physical situations, for reasoning about physical objects, and for solving problems.

As presented to you so far, dynamics has some serious shortcomings. For example, if you do not know how the net force on an object changes with time, you cannot use dynamics to determine its position or velocity at different times. In many real-world situations, from two-car collisions to the movement of countless billions of air molecules inside a balloon, we cannot hope to know the positions of, velocities of, and forces exerted on all the objects involved. However, once we decide to group objects together, we find that in many cases, something about the group stays the same. Somehow, this "something" is distributed throughout the system, and although the distribution changes as the objects interact with each other, the total amount of this "something" remains constant. This is how we recognize a conserved quantity, and also how we recognize the conditions under which this quantity is conserved. We begin with the ideas of *system*, *impulse*, and *momentum*.

3.1   SYSTEMS

In dynamics and kinematics, we were primarily interested in describing, explaining, and predicting the motion of isolated, "free" bodies as they interacted with other objects. We did so by first identifying all the forces exerted on a particular object, and then we applied Newton's Laws. We are still interested in the motion of interacting objects, except we recognize that we cannot always know the forces exerted on every object. We find that if we group selected objects into a *system*, then we can continue to describe and explain the motion of objects, even though we do not know the forces exerted on them.

Systems are usually two or more objects, such as two carts colliding with each other, but we sometimes also refer to *one-body systems*.

3.2 MOMENTUM AND IMPULSE

When two carts collide, what principle governs their behavior? Let's take the simplest case: A moving cart collides with and sticks to a second cart originally at rest, as shown. We know from experience that the resulting velocity is smaller than the velocity of the moving cart before the collision. If we vary the masses of the two carts, we get a definite pattern for the resulting velocity

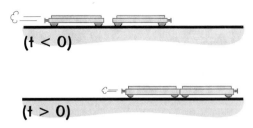

$(t < 0)$

$(t > 0)$

of the combination. We will see that the concepts of *momentum* and *impulse* are very useful for understanding the behavior of systems. We start by defining each concept using one-body systems before showing how they are used in many-body systems.

Impulse. A force tells us how hard and in what direction one object is pushing or pulling on another. We know that the larger the force, the larger the object's acceleration. We also know that the longer a force is exerted the larger the change in velocity. Consider a <u>single</u>, constant force **F** exerted on an object having mass m for a time interval Δt. The acceleration **a** is constant, with a magnitude and direction equal to **F**/m. (Newton's 2nd law, **F** = m**a**, implies that **a** = **F**/m.) The change in velocity during this process is **a**Δt, so we can write:

$$\Delta \mathbf{v} \;=\; \mathbf{a}\,\Delta t \;=\; (\mathbf{F}/m)\,\Delta t$$

Rearranging, we get: $\mathbf{F}\,\Delta t = m\,\Delta \mathbf{v}$.

The left-hand side is what we call an *impulse*. It depends on the magnitude and direction of a force and the duration of a time interval. It is a vector quantity that characterizes the overall influence of a force exerted for a certain period of time. The larger the impulse, the larger its effect on a particular object, and the larger the change in velocity.

When the force is <u>not</u> constant, we choose only very short time intervals—that is, intervals short enough that the force may be considered constant throughout the time interval. For both situations, we write:

$$\mathbf{J} \;\equiv\; \mathbf{F}\,\Delta t \qquad\qquad \textbf{definition of impulse for constant force}$$

The MKS unit of impulse is a newton-second (N-s). To calculate the impulse delivered by a constant force, simply multiply the force by the time interval over which the force is exerted. The direction of the impulse is the same as the direction of the (constant) force.

> **A 300g ball is dropped from a sixth-story window. Two seconds later it hits the ground. What is the impulse delivered by the gravitational force while the ball is falling?**
>
> (continued)

(continued)

> ***Answer.*** The gravitational force on the ball is about 3N directed straight down. The force is constant, and it is exerted for 2 seconds. The impulse delivered by the gravitational force is therefore 6N-s directed straight down.

Sometimes a force is exerted on an object, but the object does not move. We calculate the impulse in the same way as before. If you hold a 300g ball for 2 seconds, the impulse delivered by gravitation is 6N-s straight down. The ball does not move because your hand delivers an equal and opposite impulse to the ball during the same time interval. In other words, the *net impulse* is zero, resulting in no change in velocity.

In general, to calculate the net impulse, use the <u>net</u> force:

$$\mathbf{J}_{net} \equiv \mathbf{F}_{net} \, \Delta t \qquad \text{definition of net impulse for constant net force}$$

The impulse delivered by a force can be non-zero even if the <u>speed</u> of the object does not change as a result of the process:

> **A 40N wagon rolls frictionlessly along a straight horizontal sidewalk at 3m/s. An adult exerts a constant force to reverse the direction of the wagon in 0.5 seconds such that its final speed is 3m/s, but it is moving in the opposite direction. What impulse is delivered to the wagon?**
>
> > ***Answer.*** The wagon has a mass of 4kg, and its change in velocity is $\Delta \mathbf{v} = -6$m/s (i.e., 6m/s to the left). Its acceleration during the critical 0.5 seconds is $\mathbf{a} = \Delta \mathbf{v}/\Delta t = (6$m/s to the left$) / (0.5s) = 12$m/s^2 to the left. The applied force is the net force, so:
> >
> > $$\mathbf{F}_{applied} = \mathbf{F}_{net} = m\mathbf{a} = (4\text{kg})(12\text{m/s}^2 \text{ to the left}) = 48\text{N to the left}.$$
> >
> > The impulse delivered by the applied force has magnitude:
> >
> > $$J = F_{applied} \, \Delta t = (48\text{N})(0.5\text{s}) = 24\text{N-s},$$
> >
> > and is directed to the left.

Note that even though the impulse has not resulted in a change in <u>speed</u>, it has resulted in a change in <u>velocity</u>.

Momentum. For a constant force, we previously derived the relation $\mathbf{F}\Delta t = m\Delta \mathbf{v}$. The impulse $\mathbf{F}\Delta t$ causes a change in the velocity which depends on the mass of the object. The larger the mass, the smaller the change in velocity, and vice versa. We can also write:

$$\mathbf{F}\Delta t \;=\; \Delta(m\mathbf{v})$$

In other words, an impulse delivered to an object causes a change in the product $(m\mathbf{v})$. We define this product to be the *momentum* $\mathbf{p}$ of an object.

$$\mathbf{p} \;\equiv\; m\mathbf{v} \qquad\qquad \textbf{definition of momentum for single bodies}$$

To calculate the momentum of an object at a particular instant, simply multiply its mass and its velocity. The direction of the momentum is always the same as the direction of motion.

A 300g ball is dropped from a sixth-story window. Two seconds later it hits the ground. What is the momentum of the ball just before it hits the ground?

Answer. Assuming the ball is released from rest, and ignoring the effects of air resistance and buoyancy, the velocity of the ball after falling for 2 seconds is 20m/s downward. Therefore its momentum is

$$\mathbf{p} = m\mathbf{v} = 0.3\text{kg} \times 20\text{m/s} \,\langle\text{down}\rangle = 6\text{kg-m/s} \,\langle\text{down}\rangle.$$

Momentum is a vector quantity having MKS units of kilogram-meters per second (kg-m/s). The larger the mass or the velocity of an object, the larger its momentum. To help you develop a gut-level sense of what momentum means, imagine each of the following objects hitting you:

  • A fly   • A rock   • A BB shot from a gun

Both the mass and the speed of an object are important for judging momentum. A fly does not hurt when it hits you because its mass is so small. A small rock thrown just as fast will hurt more than the fly, because its mass is much larger. A BB has a small mass, but its speed is very large, so it hurts too.

When the momentum changes during a process we can calculate the <u>change</u> in momentum $\Delta\mathbf{p}$, which is also a vector quantity.

$$\Delta\mathbf{p} \;=\; \Delta(m\mathbf{v})$$

— or alternatively —

$$\Delta\mathbf{p} \;=\; \mathbf{p}_f - \mathbf{p}_i \;=\; m\mathbf{v}_f - m\mathbf{v}_i \;=\; m(\mathbf{v}_f - \mathbf{v}_i) \;=\; m\Delta\mathbf{v}$$

If either the speed or the direction of motion changes with time, then the momentum of the object changes as well:

A 40N wagon rolls frictionlessly along a straight horizontal sidewalk at 3m/s. An adult exerts a constant force to reverse the direction of the wagon in 0.5 seconds such that its final speed is 3m/s. What is the change in momentum of the wagon?

Answer. The wagon has a mass of 4kg. Its initial momentum is horizontal, so:

$$p_{ix} = mv_{ix} = (4\text{kg})(3\text{m/s}) = 12\text{kg-m/s}.$$

Its final momentum is:

$$p_{fx} = mv_{fx} = -12\text{kg-m/s}.$$

Therefore its change in momentum is:

$$\Delta p_x = p_{fx} - p_{ix} = (-12\text{kg-m/s}) - 12\text{kg-m/s} = -24\text{kg-m/s}.$$

So, $\Delta \mathbf{p} = 24\text{kg-m/s}$ to the left. (That is, $\Delta p_y = 0$.)

Note that the magnitude of the momentum has not changed, but the momentum has changed because the direction of the momentum has changed.

Sometimes, an object's momentum is constantly changing, but the change in momentum during a specified time interval is zero:

A racecar drives around a circular track at 100mph (about 45m/s). After 3 hours, the car has completed 150 laps. What is the car's change in momentum during this time period?

Answer. Even though we do not know the car's mass, we can still answer this question. As the car travels in a circle, its speed stays the same but its direction of motion is constantly changing. Similarly, its momentum is constantly changing. However, if the starting and ending velocities are the same, then the initial and final momenta are also the same. Therefore, the change in momentum for this time interval is zero.

3.3 TWO PRINCIPLES FOR DESCRIBING PHYSICAL SYSTEMS AND SOLVING PROBLEMS

The ideas of momentum and impulse lead to two new physical principles: the Impulse–Momentum Theorem, and Conservation of Momentum.

Impulse–Momentum Theorem. The net impulse delivered to an object during a particular time interval is closely related to the change in the object's momentum during the same time period. Consider the following table constructed using the examples from the previous section in which the net force was constant.

Example (pages)	$\mathbf{F}_{net}$ (N)	Δt (s)	m (kg)	$\Delta \mathbf{v}$ (m/s)	$\mathbf{J}_{net}$ (N-s)	$\Delta \mathbf{p}$ (kg-m/s)
Falling ball (R62–63,64)	3 ↓	2	0.3	20 ↓	6 ↓	6 ↓
Held ball (R63)	0	2	0.3	0	0	0
Rolling wagon (R63,65)	48 ←	0.5	4	6 ←	24 ←	24 ←

Note first that because a unit of force is equal to a unit of mass times a unit of acceleration, $1\text{N-s} = 1\text{N} \times 1\text{s} = [1\text{kg} \times 1\text{m/s}^2] \times 1\text{s} = 1\text{kg-m/s}$. Therefore the units of impulse (N-s) are equal to the units of momentum (kg-m/s).

Note also that in each case the net impulse ($\mathbf{J}_{net} = \mathbf{F}_{net}\Delta t$) is equal in both magnitude and direction to the change in momentum ($\Delta \mathbf{p} = \Delta(m\mathbf{v}) = m\Delta \mathbf{v}$). This is the Impulse–Momentum Theorem, and it is true <u>even if the force is not constant</u>. Let's see how this happens.

Remember that when the net force is not constant, we must consider very short time intervals, so that the net force can be treated as constant throughout each time interval. There is a small impulse delivered during each tiny time period, each of which causes a small change in momentum. The cumulative effect of many small impulses is the sum of all of them ($\mathbf{J}_{net}$) and the sum of all the small changes in momentum is the total change in momentum. So, we write:

$$\mathbf{J}_{net} = \Delta \mathbf{p} \qquad \textbf{Impulse–Momentum Theorem for single bodies}$$

This is a <u>vector</u> equation, and it is true component by component, as shown in the following example.

A pitcher delivers a 140g baseball at 90mph (about 40m/s). After hitting the bat, the ball goes straight up at about 30m/s. If the ball is in contact with the bat for only about two-thousandths of a second, estimate the force needed to produce the observed motion.

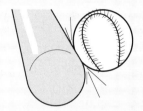

Answer. <u>Analysis</u>. The force exerted on the ball very likely changes while it is in contact with the bat. However, as an *estimate* of the force, we will assume that it is constant during the collision. Also, we will ignore all other forces on the ball, because each will be much smaller than the applied force, so the applied force is the net force. The net impulse is the product of the net force and the length of the time period ($\mathbf{J}_{net} = \mathbf{F}_{net}\,\Delta t$). The only unknown is $\mathbf{F}_{net}$. We are given enough information to calculate the change in momentum, so we can solve for $\mathbf{F}_{net}$ after applying the Impulse–Momentum Theorem.

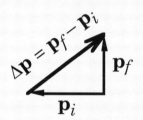

In the diagram on the left, we show how the momentum of the baseball changes during its collision with the bat. This means the net impulse delivered to the ball points in this same direction (as the change in momentum), and we should expect an applied force that points in this direction as well.

<u>Solution</u>. We choose the +x-direction to be to the right, and the +y-direction to be up. The initial velocity of the ball is (v_{ix}, v_{iy}), which is equal to (–40m/s, 0). Its final velocity is (0, 30m/s). Therefore, $\Delta v_x = v_{fx} - v_{ix} = 0\text{m/s} - (-40\text{m/s}) = 40\text{m/s}$, and $\Delta v_y = 30\text{m/s} - 0\text{m/s} = 30\text{m/s}$.

In the x-direction:
$$J_{net,x} = \Delta p_x$$
$$F_{net,x}\,\Delta t = \Delta(mv_x) = m\,\Delta v_x$$

so:
$$F_{net,x} = \frac{m\,\Delta v_x}{\Delta t} = \frac{0.14\text{kg} \times 40\text{m/s}}{0.002\text{s}} = 2800\text{N}$$

In the y-direction:
$$J_{net,y} = \Delta p_y$$
$$F_{net,y}\,\Delta t = \Delta(mv_y) = m\,\Delta v_y$$

so:
$$F_{net,y} = \frac{m\,\Delta v_y}{\Delta t} = \frac{0.14\text{kg} \times 30\text{m/s}}{0.002\text{s}} = 2100\text{N}$$

This is a force of 3500N directed at 37° above the horizontal. It is the equivalent of almost 800lb of force. We might have difficulty lifting this amount of weight, but in some cases we can exert such a force if the time period is very short.

Conservation of Momentum for two-body systems. Whenever two objects interact, each exerts a force on the other. The magnitudes of these two forces are equal in magnitude and opposite in direction, <u>instant by instant</u>. This is Newton's Third Law.

Consider two carts colliding with each other. One cart is at rest. The other cart is moving to the right, and it has a spring bumper that recoils when the two carts are in contact.

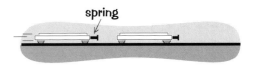

The five pictures of the two carts show how the positions of the carts change with time. The first picture is "taken" just as the carts touch each other, and the last one is taken just as they lose contact. As the carts move closer together, the spring becomes more compressed, and the spring force becomes larger, reaching its largest value at $t = 0.04$s. After this point, the right-hand cart is moving faster than the left-hand cart, so it moves away from it, eventually losing contact with the spring.

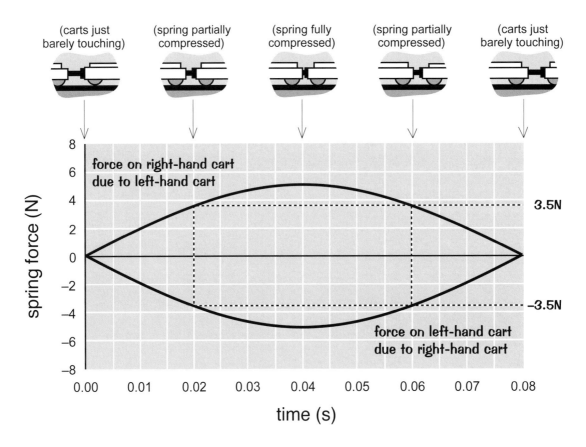

The graph shows roughly how the forces exerted on the two carts change with time. The entire "collision" takes only 8/100ths of a second to complete. When the carts are just barely touching (at $t = 0$s and at $t = 0.08$s), the spring force that each cart exerts on the other is zero. When the spring is partially compressed at 0.02s and 0.06s, the force on the right-hand cart is +3.5N (that is, 3.5N to the right), and the force on the left-hand cart is –3.5N (that is, 3.5N to the left). The largest force that each exerts on the other occurs when the spring is maximally compressed, at $t = 0.04s$. At every instant of time, the spring force on the right-hand cart is equal and opposite to the force on the left-hand cart.

This graph represents a typical collision. In most collisions, the two objects exert non-zero forces on each other only for a very short time interval, and the motion of both objects is affected. Let's use momentum and impulse ideas to help us understand collisions on a different level.

Because the forces that objects exert on each other are equal and opposite instant by instant, the impulses that they deliver to the each other during any time interval are equal and opposite as well. Using the Impulse–Momentum Theorem, this means that whenever two objects interact, the change in one object's momentum must be exactly equal and opposite to the change in the other object's momentum. Therefore, if we group all interacting objects together into a single system, then the result of each interaction is simply a transfer of momentum from one object to another. The momentum lost by one object is always gained by another. This is the principle of Conservation of Momentum.

Because we have grouped all interacting objects together, we are assuming no external forces. If we group only some interacting objects together, such as two carts rolling toward each other on a horizontal surface, then there are external forces to worry about. When the net external force is zero, the net impulse on the system is zero also, and momentum is conserved. In general, we write the Law of Conservation of Momentum as:

$$\Delta \mathbf{P}_{system} = 0$$

— or —

Conservation of Momentum when there is <u>no net external force</u>

$$\mathbf{P}_i = \mathbf{P}_f$$

where:

$\mathbf{P}_{system}$ ≡ total momentum of a system
    = sum of all the individual momenta in the system
    = $\mathbf{p}_1 + \mathbf{p}_2 + ... = m_1\mathbf{v}_1 + m_2\mathbf{v}_2 + ...$

$\mathbf{P}_i$ = total initial momentum of the system (i.e., before an interaction)

$\mathbf{P}_f$ = total final momentum of the system (i.e., after the interaction)

In all other cases, momentum is not conserved, because there is a net impulse delivered to the system. When the net impulse is very small compared to the impulses delivered by internal forces, we can say that momentum is *approximately* conserved. This happens when the net external force on the system is very small, such as when two carts roll toward each other with very little friction.

The most common application of Conservation of Momentum occurs when momentum is only approximately conserved.

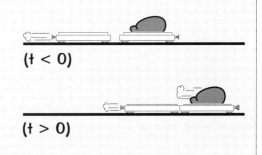

A 1kg cart rolls at 25cm/s toward a 1.5kg cart at rest. The carts stick together and proceed as shown. The net friction force exerted on the system is about 0.1N, and the collision takes about 0.1s to occur. How much momentum is lost due to friction during the collision? What is the final speed of the carts? Is momentum *approximately* conserved?

(t < 0)

(t > 0)

Answer. The net impulse delivered to the system is (0.1N to the left × 0.1s) = 0.01N-s to the left, so 0.01kg-m/s of momentum is "lost" during the collision. The initial momentum of the system is (1kg × 0.25m/s to the right) = 0.25kg-m/s to the right. The change in momentum is 0.01kg-m/s to the left, so the final momentum must be 0.24kg-m/s to the right, and the final speed of the carts is 9.6cm/s. Only 4% of the momentum is "lost" due to friction so momentum is approximately conserved. If we ignore frictional effects, we would predict a speed of 10cm/s using momentum conservation.

3.4 USING MOMENTUM IDEAS AND PRINCIPLES TO ANALYZE SITUATIONS AND SOLVE PROBLEMS

Reasoning with momentum ideas. Before learning how to use momentum and impulse ideas to solve problems, you must learn how to analyze physical situations. This is so that you can properly apply the principles presented thus far. For example, can you identify all the internal forces exerted on a system? All the external forces? What is the best choice for a system? Can you estimate the net impulse delivered to a system by external forces? All these skills (and more!) will help you solve problems more efficiently and more successfully.

SITUATIONS INVOLVING A NET IMPULSE

Most one-body systems fall into this category. When you pick up and throw a ball, the momentum of the ball is changing throughout, from the instant you pick it up until it is caught or rolls to a stop. Usually, the easiest way to tell if a net impulse is delivered is to look at the change in the momentum of the system:

You fire a 40g sponge-rubber ball horizontally with a spring-loaded gun. The speed of the ball as it leaves the gun is 5m/s. What impulse is delivered to the ball, and what combination of forces delivers the necessary impulse?

Answer. If you are not moving just before you fire the gun, the initial momentum of the ball is zero. The change in momentum is $\Delta p_x = m\Delta v_x = (0.040\text{kg} \times 5\text{m/s}) = 0.20\text{kg-m/s}$, so the gun must deliver a horizontal impulse of 0.20N-s. This is not the impulse delivered by the spring alone. Rather, it is the net impulse delivered by all external forces on the ball. This includes friction between the ball and the inside of the gun as well as air resistance.

Sometimes it is hard to tell that a net external force is present, or if it is present, what object exerts it. Keep in mind: if the momentum of the system changes, there must be a net impulse delivered to the system:

Reconsider the previous example, except consider the ball and gun as the system. What impulse is delivered to the system, and what object exerts the force that delivers this impulse?

Answer. If someone is holding the gun at rest during the entire process, then the gun's change in momentum is zero. The system's change in momentum is therefore the same as the ball's change in momentum: 0.20kg-m/s to the right. The system must experience a horizontal impulse of 0.20N-s.

The only object that can possibly exert a horizontal force to the right on the system is the person holding the gun. This horizontal force is exerted only while the ball is being shot, and prevents the gun from recoiling. No matter how short the time interval needed to shoot the ball, a horizontal force must be applied, and it must be large enough to deliver the observed impulse.

Sometimes, even though we know very little about a situation, we can still make certain comparisons using reasonable assumptions about its physical characteristics.

A basketball and a racquetball are dropped simultaneously from the same height. Which ball experiences the larger impulse when it hits the ground?

both balls are released from rest

Answer. We do not know the height at which the balls are released. However, neglecting the effects of air resistance, both balls will hit the ground with the same speed. The exact speed that each has on the way back up depends on the balls themselves. As you will see, we do not need to know exactly how fast each is moving to answer these questions.

Experience tells us that each ball will return to about the same height. Therefore, just after hitting the ground they each have the same speed. So, they both have the same velocity just before hitting the ground, and they both have the same velocity just after hitting the ground. This means they both must have the same change in velocity during the collision with the ground. Because the basketball is much heavier (by a factor of 15), its change in momentum ($M\Delta\mathbf{V}$) must be larger than the change in momentum of the racquetball ($m\Delta\mathbf{v}$). Therefore, the basketball experiences the larger impulse.

both balls return to the SAME height

Another way of making comparisons is by using *limiting cases*. If the smallest possible impulse delivered to the basketball is larger than the largest possible impulse delivered to the racquetball, then the basketball <u>always</u> experiences the larger impulse, no matter what the actual results are.

Answer. The <u>smallest</u> possible impulse delivered to the basketball occurs when it does not bounce at all; its final speed is zero. The impulse delivered by the ground is the basketball's change in momentum Mv_{max}, where v_{max} is the speed of the each ball just before it hits the ground. The <u>largest</u> possible impulse delivered to the racquetball occurs when it bounces all the way back to its original height. It certainly cannot bounce any higher than that. The racquetball's change in momentum is $2mv_{\text{max}}$. Because M is closer to $15m$ than $2m$, the impulse delivered to the basketball—even in this extreme case—is more than 7 times as large as the impulse delivered to the racquetball.

balls return to DIFFERENT heights

You must always remember that the net impulse delivered to an object ($\mathbf{F}_{net}\Delta t$) is exactly equal to the object's change in momentum ($m\Delta\mathbf{v}$). When two objects interact, each delivers an equal and opposite impulse to the other. So, if one object is much more massive than the other, the effect will be much more noticeable for the lighter object, because the change in its velocity will be so much more than the other's.

A 7kg bowling ball rolling at 2m/s hits a 1kg bowling pin. After the collision, the ball slows down to 1.5m/s, and the pin moves away at 3.5m/s. Which object experiences the larger impulse?

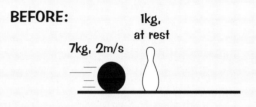

Answer. The ball's change in momentum is

$$\Delta P_x = M\Delta V_x$$
$$= (7\text{kg}) \times (1.5\text{m/s} - 2\text{m/s})$$
$$= -3.5\text{kg-m/s}$$

so it experiences an impulse of 3.5N-s directed to the left and delivered by the pin.

The pin also has a change in momentum:

$$\Delta p_x = m\Delta v_x$$
$$= (1\text{kg}) \times (3.5\text{m/s} - 0\text{m/s})$$
$$= +3.5\text{kg-m/s}$$

so it experiences an impulse of 3.5N-s directed to the right and delivered by the ball. The two objects experience <u>equal and opposite</u> impulses.

SITUATIONS IN WHICH THE NET IMPULSE IS ZERO OR VERY CLOSE TO ZERO

In all of the previous examples, we used the Impulse–Momentum Theorem to analyze the physical situations. We were required to do this because the system always experienced a net impulse. In the following examples, we can use Conservation of Momentum, because we can choose a system on which the net impulse delivered by external forces is so small that we can ignore it.

Conservation of Momentum can be particularly useful for learning about the masses of objects when we are given information about their velocities before and after a collision. An example of this is found on the next page.

Two carts—one white, one gray—are made of different materials, making one heavier than the other. In a certain collision, the white cart is moving, while the gray one is not. After the collision, the white cart slows down but continues in the same direction, and the gray cart moves off at a speed larger than the original speed of the white one. What can we say about the masses of the two carts?

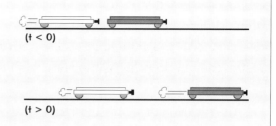

(t < 0)

(t > 0)

Answer. Assuming that frictional forces are negligible, momentum is conserved during the collision. Therefore, the initial momentum of the white cart is shared by both carts after the collision. In fact, the final momentum of the gray cart must be smaller than the initial momentum of the white one. But we observed that the final speed of the gray cart is larger than the initial speed of the white one. Therefore, the mass of the gray cart must be smaller than the mass of the white cart.

Conservation of Momentum is a vector equation, which sometimes yields some interesting comparisons.

Cart A collides with a heavier cart (B) at rest. After the collision, cart A moves to the left, as shown. What can we say about the momenta of the carts?

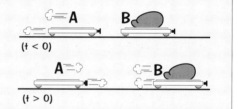

Answer. As in the previous example, momentum is conserved during the collision. At first, cart B is at rest, so all the momentum in the system is possessed by cart A. After the collision the total momentum is unchanged, but cart A has reversed directions. The only way this can happen is if the momentum of cart B after the collision is larger than the initial momentum of cart A. $(p_{B,f} > p_{A,i})$ The vector diagram at right shows why this must be true.

Also, because the total momentum in the system is directed to the right, the final momentum of cart B must be larger than the final momentum of cart A. $(p_{B,f} > p_{A,f})$

$$\mathbf{p}_{A,i} + \mathbf{p}_{B,i} = \mathbf{p}_{A,f} + \mathbf{p}_{B,f}$$

We do not have enough information to determine if the momentum of cart A becomes larger or smaller as a result the collision.

Solving problems using momentum ideas. You have been taught two new physical principles, each involving momentum, which can be used to solve problems. The first is the Impulse–Momentum Theorem, which relates the forces exerted on an object or system over a time period to the change in its momentum. The other is Conservation of Momentum, which relates the momentum of a system at one instant of time to its momentum at a later time.

USING THE IMPULSE–MOMENTUM THEOREM TO SOLVE PROBLEMS

As with most physical principles, there are different ways that the Impulse–Momentum Theorem can be used. For example, if you know the value of all the forces exerted on an object or system during a certain time interval, then you can determine the change in its momentum, and perhaps learn something about the masses or the velocities of the objects in the system. Or, if you know how the momentum of a system changes with time, you can determine the impulse delivered to the system, and perhaps learn something about the forces exerted on the system.

In the Impulse–Momentum Theorem,

$$\mathbf{F}_{net}\, \Delta t \; = \; m_1 \Delta \mathbf{v}_1 + m_2 \Delta \mathbf{v}_2 + \ldots$$

there are only four types of unknowns: forces, time intervals, masses, and velocities. If we are missing only one of the unknowns, we can use the Impulse–Momentum Theorem to find it.

A 20kg child is sitting in a 10kg wagon on a flat horizontal surface. Her older brother gives the wagon a horizontal push of 150N for one-half second. What is the speed of the wagon immediately following the push?

Answer. *Analysis*. Even though the brother is touching only the wagon, he is accelerating both the wagon and the child, so we must use $m = 30\text{kg}$. Friction is probably about 15N, which is much smaller than the applied force, so let's ignore it for simplicity. Gravitation and the normal force from the ground balance each other, so the net force is equal to the applied force, 150N. We can use this value to determine the impulse delivered by the brother. Therefore, we can determine the change in momentum of the wagon and child. We know the mass of the system and its initial velocity, therefore we can determine its final velocity, as desired.

Solution. The net force is 150N, exerted horizontally for ½ second. Therefore, using the definition of impulse (for a constant force), the net impulse on the system is $J_{net} = F_{net}\,\Delta t = (150\text{N} \times \frac{1}{2}\text{s}) = 75\text{N-s}$. By the Impulse–Momentum Theorem, this impulse must produce a change in momentum of 75kg-m/s. The mass of the system is constant at 30kg throughout, so the change in the system's velocity must be $2\frac{1}{2}$m/s, in the direction of the applied force. Because the initial velocity is zero, the final speed of the child and wagon must be $2\frac{1}{2}$m/s.

You must be very flexible in how you use the definitions of impulse and momentum and the Impulse–Momentum Theorem to solve problems. The graphic below summarizes the problem-solving strategies needed to solve problems using these ideas.

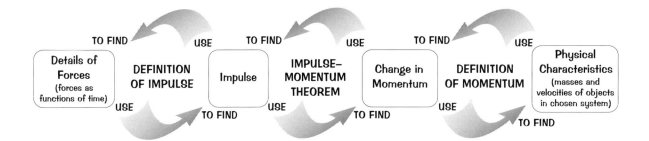

USING CONSERVATION OF MOMENTUM TO SOLVE PROBLEMS

The principle of Conservation of Momentum is usually easier to apply to situations than the Impulse–Momentum Theorem. The hard part of using this conservation principle is recognizing when it can be used and identifying the best choice for the system.

The application of Conservation of Momentum is the same in almost all cases:

- Identify the system to be considered.

- Determine if the net impulse due to external forces is small enough to ignore.

- Determine or represent the total momentum of the system at one instant of time.

- As long as the net impulse on the system is negligibly small, the momentum of the system stays the same.

As you read the following examples, keep track of these four steps, and watch how each is used to solve the problems.

The Law of Conservation of Momentum allows us to predict the motion of objects when we know the total momentum initially contained in a system.

A 1kg cart travels at 30cm/s as shown, colliding with and sticking to a 2kg cart moving to the left with the same speed. What is the final speed and direction of the pair after the collision?

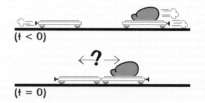

Answer. *Analysis*. Assuming friction is negligible, the net external force on the system of two carts is zero, so momentum is conserved in the collision. We have enough information to determine the initial momentum in the system. This is equal to the final momentum, so we can solve for the velocity of the two carts, as desired.

Solution. The 1kg cart has an initial momentum of 0.3kg-m/s to the right, and the 2kg cart has an initial momentum of 0.6kg-m/s to the left. The total momentum of the system is therefore 0.3kg-m/s to the left <u>at all times</u>. After the collision, both carts have the same velocity and a total mass of 3kg, so they must have a velocity of 10cm/s to the left. Mathematically:

$$[\text{final momentum}] = [\text{initial momentum}]$$

$$\mathbf{P}_f = \mathbf{P}_i$$

Taking just the horizontal component of this relation:

$$P_{fx} = P_{ix}$$

$$(m_1 + m_2)V_{fx} = m_1 v_{1x} + m_2 v_{2x}$$

Solving for the final velocity:

$$V_{fx} = \frac{m_1 v_{1x} + m_2 v_{2x}}{m_1 + m_2} = \frac{1\text{kg} \times 0.3\text{m/s} + 2\text{kg} \times (-0.3\text{m/s})}{1\text{kg} + 2\text{kg}}$$

$$= \frac{-0.3\text{kg-m/s}}{3\text{kg}}$$

$$= -10\text{cm/s}$$

After the collision, the two carts move off together at 10cm/s traveling to the left.

Conservation of Momentum is a vector equation. When the net external force has a definite direction, then the impulse delivered by that force has the same direction, and momentum is not conserved <u>only in that direction</u>. Momentum is conserved in all directions perpendicular to the direction of the net external impulse. In the following example, there is a net external force in the vertical direction. However, momentum is still conserved in the horizontal direction. Therefore, we can still predict the motion of the objects in the system:

A 500g lump of clay is dropped onto a 1kg cart traveling at 30cm/s as shown. What is the final speed and direction of the pair after the collision?

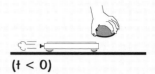

(t < 0)

Answer. *Analysis.* No matter how gently the clay is dropped onto the cart, it will have some momentum before it hits the cart. This momentum is lost due to an increased normal force exerted by the floor during the collision. However, <u>in the horizontal direction</u>, momentum is conserved, because the net impulse on the system is vertical.

(t = 0)

Solution. Just before the collision, the 1kg cart has a momentum of 0.3kg-m/s to the right, and the clay has no horizontal component of momentum. After the collision, all 1.5kg are traveling to the right and must have a total momentum of 0.3kg-m/s. Therefore, the cart and clay must be moving at 20cm/s to the right. Mathematically:

$$\left[\begin{array}{c} \text{horizontal component} \\ \text{of final momentum} \end{array} \right] = \left[\begin{array}{c} \text{horizontal component} \\ \text{of initial momentum} \end{array} \right]$$

$$P_{fx} = P_{ix}$$

$$(m + M)V_{fx} = Mv_{ix}$$

so:
$$V_{fx} = \frac{Mv_{ix}}{m + M} = \frac{1\text{kg} \times 0.3\text{m/s}}{0.5\text{kg} + 1\text{kg}} = 20\text{cm/s}$$

The cart and clay move to the right at 20cm/s after the clay is dropped onto the cart.

The process of solving problems using Conservation of Momentum is shown in the graphic below.

Summary of momentum ideas and principles. In this section, we have introduced one new "state" variable—momentum **p**—and two new "process" variables—impulse **J** and change in momentum Δ**p**. Any of the three may be used to refer to individual objects or to collections of objects (called systems). We have introduced two new physical principles—the Impulse–Momentum Theorem and Conservation of Momentum—and we have shown how the new variables are used to apply them properly. We have seen how we can describe and understand a complicated system, even if we do not know the details of the interactions between objects in that system. This means there are problems and situations for which we cannot use dynamics, yet we can still predict the motion of objects.

We now introduce some new ideas—*work*, *kinetic energy*, and *potential energy*—and show how they are used in two new physical principles—the *Work–Kinetic Energy Theorem* and *Conservation of Energy*. You will see that there are many similarities between "energy" ideas and "momentum" ideas, but there are some important differences. For example, energy is a scalar quantity, while momentum is a vector.

Energy ideas are often used in situations where both dynamics and momentum ideas are insufficient. For instance, let's say we want to estimate or predict the maximum speed of a ball as it is swinging on a string. We cannot use dynamics or momentum ideas, because we do not know how the tension force exerted by the string changes with time. However, you will see that energy ideas are enough. In fact, energy ideas can be used to determine the speed of the ball at any position along its swing!

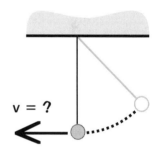

The idea of a *system* will be useful when applying energy ideas. Like momentum, we will find that energy is something that is distributed in different ways throughout a system, and that objects in the system can transfer amounts of energy between each other.

We begin with the ideas of *work* and *kinetic energy*.

3.5 WORK AND KINETIC ENERGY

Definition of work. A force is an indication of how hard and in what direction one object pulls or pushes another. Consider a wagon being pulled by a rope held at different angles. The tension and the initial velocity of the wagon are the same in each case.

Which wagons are speeding up? Which ones are slowing down? We know from dynamics that in four of the cases (A, B, D, and E), the wagon is speeding up, because the tension force on it has a component in the direction of motion. In only one case (C), the wagon is slowing down, because the tension force has a component <u>opposite</u> the direction of motion.

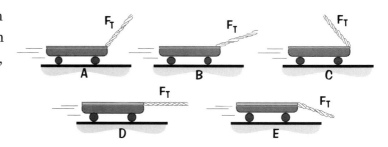

Which wagon has the largest change in speed? The rate at which something speeds up or slows down depends on the mass and the net force. In these cases, only the horizontal component of the tension force is relevant for comparing rates of speeding up or slowing down. The larger the component is, the larger the acceleration is, and the larger the change in velocity during a certain time period. Therefore, wagon D has the largest acceleration (in magnitude) and wagons A and C have the smallest.

The idea of *work* is defined to take into account the direction that a force is exerted relative to the direction of motion. It also depends on the magnitude of the force and the displacement through which the force is exerted. The larger the displacement is, the larger the amount of work done on an object. When the force is <u>not</u> constant, we choose very short displacements—so short that the force may be considered constant during the entire motion. In both cases, we can write:

$$W_F \equiv F_\parallel\, d$$

definition of work for constant force F exerted through displacement d

where:

$$F_\parallel = \underline{\text{component}} \text{ of } \mathbf{F} \text{ parallel to the displacement } \mathbf{d}$$
$$d = \underline{\text{magnitude}} \text{ of the displacement } \mathbf{d}$$

> **Note:** The displacement used in this definition is the change in position of the point at which the force is applied. Therefore, if the object deforms or rotates, the displacement used to calculate the work may be <u>different</u> than the displacement of the object.

Work is a <u>scalar</u> quantity that characterizes the influence of a force exerted for a certain displacement. The MKS unit of work is the joule (J), where 1J = 1N-m. To calculate the work done by a particular force, multiply the component of the force along the displacement by the magnitude of the displacement.

> **A 140g ball is dropped from a sixth-story window. Two seconds later it hits the ground. How much work is done on the ball by the gravitational force?**
>
> *Answer.* The gravitational force is about 1.4N straight down. The displacement is about 20m straight down. The work done by the gravitational force is therefore:
>
> $$W_g = F_{g,\parallel}\, d = (1.4\text{N} \times 20\text{m}) = 28\text{J}.$$

The component of the force "along" the direction of motion can be negative, as seen here:

> **A 140g ball is thrown straight up into the air, reaching a maximum height of 20m. How much work is done on the ball by the gravitational force as it is traveling from the ground to its maximum height?**
>
> *Answer.* The gravitational force is about 1.4N straight down. The displacement is about 20m straight up. The component of the gravitational force parallel to the displacement is –1.4N, so the work done by the gravitational force is:
>
> $$W_g = F_{g,\parallel}\, d = (-1.4\text{N} \times 20\text{m}) = -28\text{J}.$$

This means that whenever the component of the force parallel to the direction of motion is negative, the work done is also negative.

When the force is constant, the work depends on the <u>displacement</u>, not on the path taken by the object. Consider this example:

> **A 140g ball is thrown 10m to another person also standing on the ground. What is the work done by the gravitational force?**
>
> *Answer.* The gravitational force is about 1.4N straight down. Even though the ball follows a curved path from one person to the other, the ball is caught at about the same height it is thrown, so the component of the gravitational force parallel to the displacement is 0N. Therefore, the work done by the gravitational force is:
>
> $$W_g = F_{g,\parallel}\, d = (0\text{N} \times 10\text{m}) = 0\text{J}.$$

This means that whenever the force is perpendicular to the displacement (i.e., when the force has <u>no</u> component parallel to the displacement), the work done <u>by</u> that force is zero.

Sometimes it is inconvenient or difficult to determine the component of **F** parallel to the displacement **d**. In these situations, we use the component of the displacement parallel to the (constant) force, and re-write the definition of work as:

$$W_F \equiv F\, d_\parallel$$

definition of work for constant force F exerted through displacement d

where:
$$F = \underline{\text{magnitude}} \text{ of } \mathbf{F}$$
$$d_\parallel = \underline{\text{component}} \text{ of the displacement } \mathbf{d} \text{ parallel to } \mathbf{F}$$

A little geometry should convince you that this is identical to the previous definition of work. To apply this version of the definition of work, multiply the <u>magnitude</u> of the (constant) force by the <u>component</u> of the displacement parallel to the force, as shown in these two examples.

A 500g ball is thrown at 20m/s at an angle of 60° above the horizontal. What is the work done by the gravitational force from the time the ball is released until it reaches its maximum height?

Answer. The initial velocity has components 10m/s (right) and 17.3m/s (up). This means that it takes about 1.73s to reach its maximum height of about 15m. The magnitude of the (constant) force is about 5N, and the component of the displacement parallel to this force is –15m, so the work done by the gravitational force is $W_g = F_g\, d_\parallel = (5\text{N} \times -15\text{m}) = -75\text{J}$.

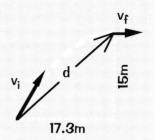

Two people are each holding 2kg books. One person slowly lifts the book directly overhead by 1m, while the other walks to the right lifting the book the same amount. Which person does more work on the book?

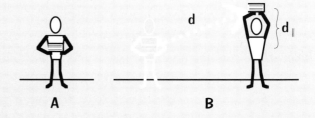

Answer. <u>Analysis</u>. Assuming that the book does not accelerate in either case, then the net force on each book is zero, and therefore, the force exerted by each person is equal and opposite the weight of each book. For situation B, we do not have enough information to find the component of **F** parallel to the displacement **d**, so we cannot use the first definition of work. However, we know the component of **d** parallel to the force **F**. Therefore, we can find the work done in each case.

> <u>Solution</u>. The work done by peron A is simply $W_A = Fd = (20\text{N} \times 1\text{m}) = 20\text{J}$. For person B, the component of **d** parallel to **F** is $d_\parallel = 1\text{m}$, so the work done is $W_B = Fd_\parallel = (20\text{N} \times 1\text{m}) = 20\text{J}$. Each person does the <u>same</u> amount of work on the book.

Note that in the last example, the work done by each person is positive, but there is no change in the speed of the object. This is because the gravitational force does an equal amount of negative work, resulting in a *total work* equal to zero. In general, to find the total work, use the work done by all the forces:

$$W_{\text{total}} \equiv F_{1,\parallel}\, d_1 + F_{2,\parallel}\, d_2 + \ldots$$

**definition of total work
for constant forces $\mathbf{F}_1$, $\mathbf{F}_2$, ...
exerted through displacements $\mathbf{d}_1$, $\mathbf{d}_2$, ...**

where:

$$F_{1,\parallel} = \underline{\text{component}} \text{ of } \mathbf{F}_1 \text{ parallel to } \mathbf{d}_1$$
$$d_1 = \underline{\text{magnitude}} \text{ of } \mathbf{d}_1$$
$$F_{2,\parallel} = \underline{\text{component}} \text{ of } \mathbf{F}_2 \text{ parallel to } \mathbf{d}_2$$
$$d_2 = \underline{\text{magnitude}} \text{ of } \mathbf{d}_2$$

(etc.)

In the special case that the object does not deform or rotate, then every part of the object undergoes the exact same displacement. Therefore, every force on the object is exerted through the same displacement. This means that we can factor the displacement out of the previous expression and re-write it using the net force as:

$$W_{\text{total}} = F_{\text{net},\parallel}\, d$$

(total work for constant $\mathbf{F}_{\text{net}}$
when the object does not deform
and does not rotate)

where:

$$F_{\text{net},\parallel} = \underline{\text{component}} \text{ of } \mathbf{F}_{\text{net}} \text{ parallel to } \mathbf{d}$$
$$d = \underline{\text{magnitude}} \text{ of } \mathbf{d}$$

Sometimes it is more convenient to use the magnitude of the net force and the component of the displacement parallel to the net force:

$$W_{\text{total}} = F_{\text{net}}\, d_{\parallel}$$

(total work for constant $\mathbf{F}_{\text{net}}$
when the object does not deform
and does not rotate)

where:

$$F_{\text{net}} \equiv \underline{\text{magnitude}} \text{ of } \mathbf{F}_{\text{net}}$$
$$d_{\parallel} = \underline{\text{component}} \text{ of } \mathbf{d} \text{ parallel to } \mathbf{F}_{\text{net}}$$

Note that these expressions are <u>not</u> definitions, and that they can only be used when the object does not deform and does not rotate. We apply them in the same way as we applied the definition of work.

<u>Sometimes</u>, a force does no total work because the overall displacement is zero. Consider this:

> **A person throws a 140g ball straight up into the air with an initial speed of 15m/s. Three seconds later, she catches the ball again. How much total work is done on the ball while it is in the air?**
>
> ***Answer.*** Neglecting air resistance, the only force on the ball while it is in the air is the force of gravitation, so the net force on the ball is constant at about 1.4N straight down. The displacement is zero, even though the total distance traveled is not. So, the total work done on the ball is $W_{total} = F_{net, \parallel} \, d = (1.4N \times 0m) = 0J$.

Calculating the work done by common interactions. Here are some examples of how to determine the work done by the forces you usually encounter: gravitation, the normal force, the tension force, static friction, and the spring force. Also, we will show why you <u>cannot</u> usually determine the work done by kinetic friction.

WORK DONE BY THE GRAVITATIONAL FORCE

You have already seen some examples of how to calculate the work done by the gravitational force. The work done by gravitation is particularly easy because the force is constant near the surface of the earth. Applying <u>either</u> definition always gives the same result:

$$W_g = -mg\Delta y \qquad \text{\textbf{work done by gravitation on a single object}}$$

where:
- m = mass of the object
- g = gravitational constant (about 10N/kg near the surface of the earth)
- Δy = <u>change</u> in height of the object

The minus sign means that when the height of the object increases, the work done by the gravitational force is negative, and when the height decreases, the work done is positive.

> **A 25g marble is released from rest on a curved track as shown. What is the work done on the marble by the force of gravitation from the time the marble is released until it reaches the end of the track?**
>
> ***Answer.*** The work done by the gravitational force depends only on the mass and the overall change in height, which is −40cm in this case. Therefore, $W_g = -(0.025kg \times 10N/kg \times -0.40m) = 0.10J$. The work done by gravitation on the marble is about $^1/_{10}J$.

In many (but not all) situations, the work done by the normal force is easily determined, because the force is often perpendicular to the displacement. This means that the component of the normal force parallel to the displacement is zero, which means the work done by the normal force is zero as well.

Consider a block sliding down a curved track. The normal force is constantly changing in both magnitude and direction, <u>but</u> at each instant it points perpendicular to the surface. Also at each instant the velocity is parallel to the surface. Because the force is changing, we must consider tiny time intervals. For each tiny Δt, the block moves through a displacement $\mathbf{v}\Delta t$, which is parallel to $\mathbf{v}$. The normal force is "constant" during this tiny Δt and it points perpendicular to the surface, and therefore perpendicular to the displacement $\mathbf{v}\Delta t$. The work done during this interval of time is zero because there is no component of the normal force along the displacement. Because this is true for every time interval, when we add them all up, the total work done by the normal force is zero.

However, there are many situations in which the normal force does work, as shown in the following example.

Two boxes are pushed on a frictionless floor, with the force being applied to box A as shown. What forces do non-zero work on box B? Is the work done by each force positive or negative?

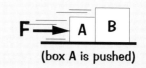

(box A is pushed)

Answer. There are three forces exerted on box B. They are: (1) a gravitational force exerted by the earth, (2) a normal force exerted by the floor on B, and (3) a normal force exerted by box A on B. (The applied force F is exerted only on box A.) The work done by forces (1) and (2) are each zero because each force is perpendicular to the displacement at all times. The work done by force (3) is positive, because the normal force exerted by A and the displacement are both in the same direction. (Both are to the right.)

When the surface exerting a normal force does not move during the interaction, the normal force does <u>no</u> work.

A lump of clay is thrown against a brick wall as shown, where it sticks. What is the work done by the wall?

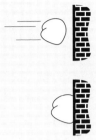

Answer. The normal force exerted by the wall on the clay is not exerted through any displacement, because the wall does not move. Therefore, the work done by the normal force is zero.

The brick wall clearly has an effect on the motion of the clay. If the wall does no work on the clay, then what <u>does</u> the wall do, and why does the clay stop?

Answer. The normal force causes the clay to slow down and stop. The normal force also delivers an impulse to the clay to cause its change in momentum. The clay stops (in part) because it is able to deform.

WORK DONE BY THE TENSION FORCE

Like the normal force, there are a number of common situations in which the tension force on an object is perpendicular to its velocity, causing the total work done by tension to be zero. For example, as an object swings in a circle, the tension force is constantly changing, but the total work done by the tension force is zero, because the force is perpendicular to the object's displacement. However, the work done by the tension force is not always zero.

In some common situations, the angle that the rope makes is important.

A wagon is moving to the right initially at 3m/s, and is pulled as shown with a tension in the rope of 20N. How much work is done on the wagon by the tension force while the wagon moves 2m?

Answer. The vertical component of the tension force on the wagon is $(20N \times \sin 50°)$ $= (20N \times 0.766) = 15.3N$. The horizontal component of the tension force is $-(20N \times \cos 50°) = -(20N \times 0.643) = -12.86N$. Only the horizontal component is needed to find the work done by the tension force: $W_T = F_{T,\parallel} d = (-12.9N \times 2m) =$ (about) $-26J$.

The work done by the rope is negative, because the displacement and the horizontal component of the tension force point in opposite directions.

If the string (or rope, etc.) is massless and does not stretch, then the <u>total work</u> done by the string (on all objects it interacts with) is zero, as shown in this example:

Two masses are attached to opposite ends of a string, which passes over a "massless" pulley as shown. The system is released from rest. When the 2kg block falls 0.4m, what is the <u>sign</u> (+ or −) of the work done by the tension force on each block, and what is the total work done by the tension force?

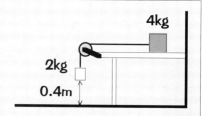

Answer. Because the pulley is massless, the tension is the same everywhere in the string. Because the string does not stretch, the 4kg block always moves the same distance as the 2kg block. As the 2kg block falls 0.4m, the tension force is opposite the displacement, so the work done is negative: $W_{T,2} = (-F_{T,2} \times 0.4\text{m})$. As the 4kg block moves to the left 0.4m, the tension force is in the same direction as the displacement, so the work done is positive: $W_{T,4} = (+F_{T,4} \times 0.4\text{m})$. The total work done by the tension force is the sum of these two:

$$W_{T,\text{total}} = W_{T,2} + W_{T,4} = (-F_{T,2} \times 0.4\text{m}) + (+F_{T,4} \times 0.4\text{m}) = (F_{T,4} - F_{T,2})(0.4\text{m})$$

Neglecting the masses of the string and the pulley, the tension is the same everywhere in the string, so the total work done is zero. *No total work is done by the tension force.*

Note that the string does non-zero work on each of the two blocks, but the <u>total</u> work done by the string is zero. Note also that even though we do not know the value of the tension force, we can still determine the total work done by the string, because the tension is the same everywhere in the string and because each block moves through the same distance.

WORK DONE BY THE FRICTION FORCE (STATIC AND KINETIC)

There are two types of friction forces: static and kinetic. Static friction is like the tension force: In certain circumstances, the static friction force can do non-zero work on an object, but the <u>total</u> work done by static friction (on the two objects interacting) is always zero. Here's an example.

Two masses are pulled as shown by a rope having a tension of 5N. The 2kg block does not slip on the 3kg slab. The floor is frictionless. When the system moves 3m, what is the work done by the static friction force on each object, and what is the total work done by static friction?

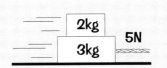

> ***Answer.*** *Analysis*. Because the floor is frictionless, the net force on the system is 5N to the right. Because the block and slab move as one, we can treat them as a single body, with a total mass of 5kg. This means their accelerations are exactly the same. The force that accelerates the 2kg block is static friction, directed to the right. The static friction force on the 3kg slab is equal in magnitude and directed to the left.
>
> _Solution_. The net force on the two blocks is 5N, directed to the right, so their acceleration is 1m/s^2, and therefore, the static friction force on the 2kg block is 2N. This force is in the same direction as the displacement, so $W_{fs,2} = (+2\text{N} \times 3\text{m}) = 6\text{J}$. The static friction force on the 3kg slab points in the opposite direction as the displacement, so $W_{fs,3} = (-2\text{N} \times 3\text{m}) = -6\text{J}$. The total work done by the static friction force is $W_{\text{total},fs} = W_{fs,2} + W_{fs,3} = 6\text{J} + (-6\text{J}) = 0\text{J}$. *Static friction does no total work on the objects that are interacting.*

A kinetic friction force is exerted whenever two objects slide across each other <u>and</u> there is a normal force exerted as a result of the contact. (Sometimes we minimize the friction force or say that it is zero, but in fact, it is always there, and is at best negligible compared to the other forces in the situation.) When determining the work done by a force, we look at the displacement of the point at which the force is exerted. With all the other forces, we did not worry about what is going on at the molecular level, because we believe that the displacement of each of the molecules is the same as the displacement of the object. Kinetic friction is different. We believe that friction arises due to a disturbance of the molecules in the surfaces touching each other. This means that the displacements of the molecules exerting forces on each other are not necessarily equivalent or the same as the displacement of the objects as a whole. Because we cannot, in general, determine the displacements of the molecules interacting to produce the friction force, we cannot, in general, determine the work done by the kinetic friction force. In a later section, we will demonstrate that this is true.

The spring force is not a constant, but changes as the length of the spring changes from its relaxed length. In general, it is difficult to calculate the work done by a spring using the definition of work, so we provide one example in which the calculation is relatively easy.

A 400g toy car is pressed up against a spring of spring constant 25N/cm, and released from rest. The relaxed length of the spring is 30cm, and initially it is compressed 10cm. How much total work is done by the spring force?

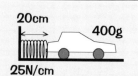

Answer. <u>Analysis</u>. Initially the spring force exerted on the car is 250N. As the car moves away from the wall, the spring gets longer, which reduces the spring force. In fact, the spring force decreases linearly, as shown in the diagram below. (When the car has moved 10cm, the spring is relaxed, so the spring force is zero.) The spring force on the car is in the same direction as its displacement. The work done on the car by the spring is the area below the force vs. displacement graph (shown in dark gray).

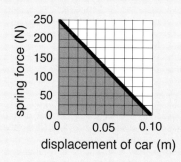

<u>Solution</u>. The area of the dark gray triangle is $\frac{1}{2}(0.10\text{m} \times 250\text{N}) = 12\frac{1}{2}\text{N-m}$, so the work done on the car by the spring force is $W_s = 12\frac{1}{2}\text{J}$. The spring also exerts a force on the wall, but the displacement of the wall is zero, so the work done on it is zero. The total work done by the spring is $12\frac{1}{2}\text{J}$.

Kinetic energy. When forces do work on an object, "something" changes. If the object is rigid and does not rotate, then we can use dynamics and kinematics to determine what that "something" is. Let's look again at some of the situations we have seen so far in the examples. In particular, let's look at the <u>total</u> work and at how the <u>speed</u> of the object changes in each case:

Example (page)	W_{total} (J)	v_i (m/s)	v_f (m/s)	m (kg)	$(v_f)^2 - (v_i)^2$ (m²/s²)	$(v_f - v_i)^2$ (m²/s²)
ball dropped (R81)	28	0	20	0.14	400	400
ball thrown straight up (R81)	–28	20	0	0.14	–400	400
ball thrown at an angle (R82)	–75	20	10	0.5	–300	100
book lifted up (R82)	0	0	0	2	0	0
ball thrown and caught (R83)	0	15	15	0.14	0	0

What is the expression that relates the total work done on an object to the initial and final speeds? In the first 3 cases, the total work is equal to one-half of the mass multiplied by the <u>change</u> in v^2. The "something" that changes when total work is done on a rigid, non-rotating object is the quantity $\frac{1}{2}mv^2$, which we call the *kinetic energy*:

$$E_K \equiv \frac{1}{2}mv^2 \qquad \textbf{definition of kinetic energy for a rigid, non-rotating object}$$

where: m = mass of the object

   v = <u>speed</u> of the object

Note that the factor of 1/2 is <u>essential</u> for being able to equate the total work to the change in kinetic energy. Also note that when <u>no</u> total work is done, there is no change in kinetic energy as shown in the last two examples above.

Kinetic energy is a <u>scalar</u> quantity. It can never be negative, because it depends only on quantities that are always positive, but the <u>change</u> in kinetic energy <u>can</u> be negative. The MKS unit for kinetic energy is the same as for work: the joule (J). (1J = 1N-m = 1kg-m²/s²) During a process we can calculate the <u>change</u> in kinetic energy by subtracting the initial kinetic energy from the final kinetic energy:

$$\Delta E_K = \Delta(\frac{1}{2}mv^2)$$

— or —

$$\Delta E_K = E_{K,f} - E_{K,i} = \frac{1}{2}m(v_f)^2 - \frac{1}{2}m(v_i)^2 = \frac{1}{2}m\left[(v_f)^2 - (v_i)^2\right] = \frac{1}{2}m\Delta(v^2)$$

Note that the change in v^2 is different than the (change in v)², as shown in the last column of the previous table.

The kinetic energy of an object changes <u>only</u> when the speed changes.

A superball bounces off a wall, rebounding with the same speed but the opposite direction it had before. What is the change in its kinetic energy?

Answer. Because the speed of the superball has not changed, the change in its kinetic energy is zero.

If the kinetic energy does not change, then what <u>does</u> change as a result of hitting the wall?

Answer. Both the velocity and the momentum of the ball change.

For an object that deforms or rotates, and also for a system of objects, we think of the object or system as a collection of rigid, non-rotating objects. To find the <u>total</u> kinetic energy, we simply add up the kinetic energies of all the parts of the object or system:

$$E_{K,\text{total}} \equiv \tfrac{1}{2}m_1(v_1)^2 + \tfrac{1}{2}m_2(v_2)^2 + \dots$$

definition of <u>total</u> kinetic energy for a collection of rigid, non-rotating objects

where:
$$m_1 = \text{mass of "object" 1}$$
$$v_1 = \text{speed of "object" 1}$$
$$m_2 = \text{mass of "object" 2}$$
$$v_2 = \text{speed of "object" 2}$$

(etc.)

Two small metal balls are connected to a light rod and are spinning around its center at 20cm/s. Estimate the total kinetic energy of the system?

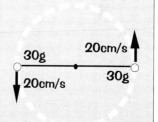

Answer. Ignoring the kinetic energy of the rod (its mass is negligible), the total kinetic energy is simply the sum of the kinetic energies of the two balls. Assuming that every part of both balls is moving at 20cm/s, we can use:

$$E_{K,\text{total}} = \tfrac{1}{2}m_1(v_1)^2 + \tfrac{1}{2}m_2(v_2)^2$$

$$= \tfrac{1}{2}(0.03\text{kg})(0.2\text{m/s})^2 + \tfrac{1}{2}(0.03\text{kg})(0.2\text{m/s})^2$$

$$= 0.0012\text{J}$$

Note that even though the balls are moving in opposite directions, the kinetic energies are equal, so the total kinetic energy is twice the kinetic energy of each.

3.6 TWO MORE PRINCIPLES FOR DESCRIBING PHYSICAL SYSTEMS AND SOLVING PROBLEMS

The ideas of work and kinetic energy lead to two new physical principles—the Work–Kinetic Energy Theorem and the Law of Conservation of Energy—and two new forms of energy: *potential energy* and *microscopic energy*.

Work–Kinetic Energy Theorem. In the table of examples on page R90, the total work done on each rigid, non-deformable object was equal to the change in its kinetic energy. We call this relationship the *Work–Kinetic Energy Theorem*:

$$W_{\text{total}} = \Delta E_K \qquad \text{**Work–Kinetic Energy Theorem for a rigid, non-rotating object**}$$

This relationship is true for all objects (even those that deform and rotate) and also for systems of objects, because it is true for each individual part of the object or system. It is also true when the forces exerted are not constant, as long as we consider displacements small enough to treat the force as constant during that motion. So:

$$W_{\text{total}} = \Delta E_{K,\text{total}} \qquad \text{**Work–Kinetic Energy Theorem for all objects and systems of objects**}$$

The Work–Kinetic Energy Theorem is a <u>scalar</u> equation. Keep in mind that the total work is the sum of the work done by every force, both internal and external, exerted on every object in the system.

Free-body diagrams are often helpful for determining the total work done on a system or object.

Two masses are attached to opposite ends of a string, which passes over a "massless" pulley as shown. The system is released from rest. After the 2kg block falls 0.4m, what is its speed?

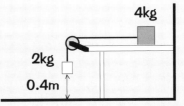

Answer. There are only 2 forces exerted on the hanging mass, as shown in the free-body diagram to the right. Its displacement is $d = 0.4$m down, which is in the same direction as gravitation, but in the opposite direction as the tension force. The work done by gravitation is $-m_1 g \Delta y_1 = m_1 g d = 8$J. The work done by the tension force is $-F_{T1}d$. (We do not know the tension, but we do not need to know it.) There are 3 forces on the sliding mass. Its displacement is 0.4m to the left, which is in the same

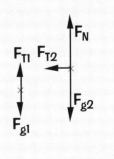

(continued)

(continued)

direction as the tension force, but perpendicular to the normal and gravitational forces. The work done by tension is $+F_{T2}d$, and the work done by the normal and gravitational forces are both zero. No work is done on the pulley, the string, or the table. The tension in the string is the same everywhere (i.e., $F_{T1} = F_{T2}$), so the two amounts of work done by the string cancel each other out. Therefore, the total work done on the system is the work done by gravitation: 8J.

By the Work–Kinetic Energy Theorem, this must be equal to the change in the total kinetic energy of the system. At any particular time, the two masses have the same speed, so the total kinetic energy is $\frac{1}{2}(m_1 + m_2)v^2 = (3\text{kg})v^2$. The initial kinetic energy is zero, so the final kinetic energy is equal to 8J when the hanging mass hits the ground, which gives us a speed of about 160cm/s. Mathematically:

$$W_{\text{total}} = \Delta E_{K,\text{total}}$$

$$W_{g1} + W_{T1} + W_{T2} + W_{g2} + W_N = E_{K,\text{final}} - E_{K,\text{initial}}$$

$$(m_1gd) + (-F_{T1}d) + (F_{T2}d) + (0) + (0) = \left[\frac{1}{2}m_1v_{\text{final}}^2 + \frac{1}{2}m_2v_{\text{final}}^2\right] - (0)$$

Simplifying and solving for v_{final}, we get:

$$v_{\text{final}} = \sqrt{\frac{2m_1gd}{m_1 + m_2}} = \sqrt{\frac{2(2\text{kg})(10\text{N/kg})(0.4\text{m})}{2\text{kg} + 4\text{kg}}} = 1.63\text{m/s}$$

Both blocks are moving at about 160cm/s when the hanging mass hits the ground.

In the following example, we show how to estimate the total work done on an object without knowing anything about the forces actually doing the work.

A 200g superball hits a wall with a speed of 80cm/s, rebounding with the same speed but the opposite direction it had before. What is the total work done on the superball from the time it first hits the wall until (a) it stops (before rebounding), and (b) it loses contact with the wall?

Answer. The total work is equal to the change in the kinetic energy of the superball: (a) $\frac{1}{2}(0.2\text{kg})(0\text{m/s})^2 - \frac{1}{2}(0.2\text{kg})(0.8\text{m/s})^2 = 0\text{J} - 0.064\text{J} = -0.064\text{J}$. (b) In this case, the initial and final speeds are the same, so $\Delta E_K = 0$. Therefore, $W_{\text{total}} = 0$.

In part (a) above, the normal force exerted by the wall does <u>no</u> work, even though it delivers an impulse to the ball. The work done on the ball is done by forces within the ball, and is exhibited by the deformation of the ball when it is touching the wall.

Often times, the force or forces that do work on an object are hard to determine, and the force that appears to do work does none, as shown in the following example.

> **A car has stopped at a traffic light. After starting up again, the car reaches a speed of 35mph. What is the force that causes the car to speed up? What is the work done by this force? What is the impulse delivered by this force?**
>
> *Answer.* Assuming that the tires do not slip, the force that causes the car to speed up is a static friction force exerted by the road on the tires. The static friction force is pointed in the <u>same</u> direction as the motion of the car. Because the road does not move, the static friction force is not exerted through any displacement, so the work done by static friction is zero.
>
> The static friction force delivers an impulse to the car, because it is delivered in the same direction during the entire motion of the car, and it is delivered for a definite period of <u>time</u>. We cannot determine the impulse delivered by static friction, because air resistance is also exerted on the car. But we <u>can</u> say that the impulse is non-zero and in the direction of the car's motion.
>
> You might think that the static friction force provides the energy needed to change the kinetic energy of the car, but this is wrong. The forces that change the kinetic energy of the car are within the car (i.e., in the engine).

As stated earlier, the work done by <u>kinetic</u> friction cannot usually be determined. Consider the following example. A box is pulled along a rough table at constant speed as shown. The work done by the force F after pulling the box a distance D is $W_F = FD$. The force of friction is exactly equal and opposite the force F.

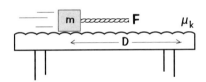

Because the box is moving with constant speed, it <u>would appear</u> that the total kinetic energy is constant. However, we know that the molecules on the bottom of the box are agitated as a result of kinetic friction, which means that the kinetic energy of those molecules increases, so the change in total kinetic energy is <u>not</u> zero. The *macroscopic* kinetic energy stays the same, but the *microscopic* kinetic energy is increasing due to friction. Therefore, the total work done on this system is <u>not</u> zero, and the work done by the friction force is <u>not</u> $-FD$.

Look also at the forces on the table. It is not moving, so the net force on it is zero. It would appear, therefore, that there is no work done on it. But work <u>is</u> done by the force of kinetic friction, because its molecules also are agitated by the box sliding over it, but we do not know how much work is done, and we do not know how to determine it. Therefore, in general, we cannot determine the work done by kinetic friction. In the next section, however, we will find that there is a way to determine the effect of kinetic friction on a system.

Conservation of Energy. Like momentum, there is a conservation law involving energy. However, unlike momentum conservation, this law is very difficult to prove, even though scientists believe it is true in all circumstances.

LAW OF CONSERVATION OF ENERGY

**Energy can be neither created nor destroyed.
The total amount of energy in the universe is constant.
Only the distribution of energy can change.**

When one object does work on another object, energy is transferred from one to the other, changing the distribution of energy in the universe. When you throw a ball, it is easy to see that the ball has gained kinetic energy, but where did the energy come from? And when you lift a box off the floor, you are doing work, but the box does not gain kinetic energy, so where did the energy go? Finally, when a car slides to a stop, it certainly loses lots of kinetic energy, so where did that energy go? To answer these questions, we must introduce some new ideas— *potential energy* and *microscopic energy*. These ideas will also help us to apply Conservation of Energy to actual situations.

Potential energy. When you lift an object, you (typically) do an amount of work on the object equal to the weight of the object (mg) multiplied by the change in height of the object (Δy). Typically, the initial and final kinetic energies are both zero, so there is no change in kinetic energy. If energy is conserved, where does the energy go?

For certain interactions, such as gravitation and springs, the work you do <u>against</u> it is stored, and can be released at a later time. When you do work against the gravitational force of the earth, *gravitational potential energy* is stored. The amount of stored energy is exactly equal to the amount of work you do on the object <u>without changing its kinetic energy</u>. So, for example, when an object is slowly lifted, its <u>change</u> in gravitational potential energy is:

$$\Delta U_g = mg\Delta y$$

where:

m = mass of the object

g = gravitational constant (about 10N/kg near the earth)

Δy = <u>change</u> in height of the object

From this we define the gravitational potential energy:

$$U_g = mgy$$

**gravitational potential energy for an object
near the earth or other celestial body**

where:

y = height of the object <u>relative to a well defined reference height</u>

It is important to keep the reference height the same throughout the analysis of any particular situation. Consider the following comparison:

Two identical balls are held as shown. Which ball has the greater gravitational potential energy?

  Answer. Neither! They both have the <u>same</u> gravitational potential energy, because they have the same mass ("identical") and are at the same height above level ground. If they were released, they would have the same speed at all heights above level ground, as potential energy is converted into kinetic energy. Although ball A has farther to travel before hitting the ground, we cannot use the bottom of the valley to determine its potential energy.

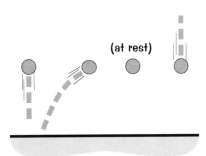

The motion of the object also does not affect the gravitational potential energy. In all of the cases shown to the left, the gravitational potential energies are the same (assuming the balls are identical), because their heights above the ground are all the same.

The gravitational potential energy is negative when the object is below the reference height, as shown in the example below.

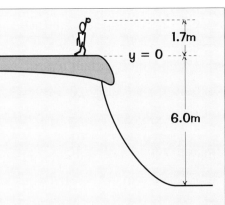

A 500g ball is thrown off a cliff as shown. What is the gravitational potential energy of the ball (a) just as it is released, and (b) just before it hits the ground at the bottom of the cliff?

  Answers.
  (a) Using the given reference height indicated in the diagram (i.e., $y = 0$), the initial height of the ball is $y_a = 1.7\text{m}$, so:

  $$U_{g,a} = mgy_a = (0.5\text{kg} \times 10\text{N/kg} \times 1.7\text{m}) = 8.5\text{J}.$$

  (b) The "height" of the ball just before it hits the ground at the bottom of the cliff is $y_b = -6.0\text{m}$, so:

  $$U_{g,b} = mgy_b = (0.5\text{kg} \times 10\text{N/kg} \times -6.0\text{m}) = -30\text{J}.$$

We can also store energy in springs. To find the potential energy in a spring, we must go back to the spring force and imagine doing work against this force. When the spring is unstretched, it exerts no force and it stores no energy. When you push or pull on a spring, the force increases linearly according to $F_s = kd$, where k is the "spring constant" or "elastic constant", and d is how far you have pushed or pulled the spring. Because the force is changing, the work done is not so easy to determine. We must imagine very small displacements—displacements so small that the spring force may be considered constant during it. The work done is the area below a graph of force vs. displacement.

The diagram on the right shows the configuration we are working with. A spring is against a wall and we are pushing on the other end of it, slowly compressing the spring. Initially the spring is unstretched, and the applied force is zero. As we compress the spring, the force we must apply increases. After compressing the spring a distance d, the applied force has increased to kd. The work done is the area below the force vs. distance graph, as shown below in white.

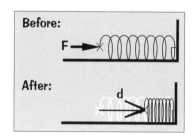

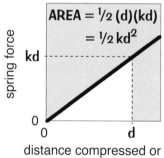

distance compressed or stretched from relaxed state

The work done on the spring is $\frac{1}{2}kd^2$, and therefore, this is the amount of potential energy now stored in the spring.

Positive work is also done when the spring is stretched from its relaxed state, because the applied force and the displacement are again in the same direction (that is, to the left). Therefore, the same expression can be used to find the potential energy stored in a spring whether the spring is stretched or compressed from its relaxed condition.

$$U_s = \frac{1}{2}kd^2 \qquad \textbf{spring (or elastic) potential energy}$$

where: $\qquad k$ = spring constant
$\qquad\qquad d$ = distance the spring is stretched or compressed from its relaxed state

Sometimes it is more convenient to write the spring potential energy in terms of the actual length (L) and relaxed length (L_0) of the spring:

$$U_s = \frac{1}{2}k(L - L_0)^2 \qquad \textbf{spring (or elastic) potential energy}$$

The spring potential energy depends only on the spring constant and the change in length of the spring. It does not depend on how the spring came to be in the state it is in, as shown in the following example.

A 6cm-long spring is lying relaxed as shown. What is the potential energy stored in the spring when its loose end is placed on the other hook? (The hooks are 10cm apart.)

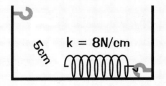

k = 8N/cm

5cm

> ***Answer.*** Even though the end of the spring is moved 5cm, this is <u>not</u> the amount the spring is stretched from its relaxed state. When the spring is on both hooks, its length is $L = 10$cm, and its relaxed length is $L_0 = 6$cm, so its extension is <u>4cm</u>, and its spring potential energy is:
>
> $$U_s = \tfrac{1}{2}k(L-L_0)^2 = \tfrac{1}{2}(800\text{N/m})(0.10\text{m}-0.06\text{m})^2 = \tfrac{1}{2}(800\text{N/m})(0.04\text{m})^2 = 0.64\text{J}.$$

We take the relaxed length to be the reference point, so the spring potential energy is always positive when it is stretched or compressed, and is always zero when the spring is relaxed. Only the <u>change</u> in spring potential energy can be negative.

A 1kg ball is sitting at rest on a spring as shown. How much potential energy is stored in the spring?

1kg

8N/cm

> ***Answer.*** Even though we do not know the length or the relaxed length of the spring, we do know how far it is compressed from its relaxed state: The weight of the ball is 10N, so the spring must be compressed by $1\tfrac{1}{4}$cm in order to keep the ball in equilibrium. So, the spring potential energy is:
>
> $$U_s = \tfrac{1}{2}k(L-L_0)^2 = \tfrac{1}{2}(800\text{N/m})(0.0125\text{m})^2 = 0.0625\text{J}.$$

Note that even though the spring is compressed, the spring potential energy is positive.

Microscopic vs. macroscopic energy. In most of the examples and expressions given so far, we have neglected and ignored an entire realm—the microscopic. Even when an object, such as a ball, is at rest, the atoms and molecules that make it up are moving. Therefore, these microscopic particles have kinetic energy. These atoms and molecules interact with each other, and are held together by very strong attractive forces. (Imagine how much work you would have to do to pull apart something into a lot of very small pieces.) Therefore, there is also potential energy between these microscopic particles. Unfortunately, we cannot write down a general expression for the kinetic and potential energies of an object due to the motion and interactions of microscopic particles. But we can sometimes determine how much energy has been transferred from the macroscopic realm to the microscopic. For example, when a box sliding along the floor slows down and stops, it has lost all of its kinetic energy, but it has gained no potential energy. The energy has been deposited into the two surfaces in contact, causing increased motion of the molecules, which can sometimes be perceived as a higher temperature. When a skydiver is falling at terminal velocity, her macroscopic kinetic energy is constant, but her gravitational potential energy is steadily decreasing. The potential energy lost as she is falling is gained by individual molecules. Another source of microscopic energy is sound, so when two objects collide making a huge crashing noise, you know that energy has been transferred from the objects to the surroundings.

TOTAL ENERGY
(E_{total})

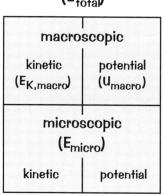

Even though there are really only two types of energy—kinetic and potential—it is often convenient to separate each type into *macroscopic* and *microscopic*. The expressions we have been using are for <u>macroscopic</u> energy only. There are no general expressions for either the microscopic kinetic or potential energies. The *total energy* can be written with three terms:

$$E_{total} \equiv E_{K,macro} + U_{macro} + E_{micro}$$
definition of <u>total</u> energy

where:

$E_{K,macro}$ = total macroscopic kinetic energy

U_{macro} = total macroscopic potential energy
(includes both spring and gravitational)

E_{micro} = total microscopic energy
(includes both kinetic and potential energy)

(Often, we drop the "macro" labels and denote these as E_K, U, and E_{micro}.)

The total energy is the quantity that remains constant. Therefore, this is the quantity we must use to write down the Law of Conservation of Energy:

$$\Delta E_{total} = 0 \qquad \textbf{Law of Conservation of Energy}$$

— or alternatively —

$$E_{total,f} = E_{total,i}$$

— or —

$$\Delta E_{K,macro} + \Delta U_{macro} + \Delta E_{micro} = 0$$

— or even —

$$E_{K,f} + U_f + E_{micro,f} = E_{K,i} + U_i + E_{micro,i}$$

All of these forms are equivalent, but <u>you</u> must decide which form is best when applying the Law of Conservation of Energy to a particular situation.

3.7 USING ENERGY IDEAS AND PRINCIPLES TO ANALYZE SITUATIONS

Before learning how to solve problems using energy, you must learn how to analyze physical situations. This is so that you will know which energy concepts and principles are appropriate and so that you will apply the energy principles properly.

Analyzing situations using the Work–Kinetic Energy Theorem. Whenever the kinetic energy of an object changes, we know that work has been done on it. The larger the change in kinetic energy is, the larger the total work is.

> **Two identical carts (A and B) are rolling with the same initial speed, when Alicia and Brian each stop one of the carts. If cart B rolls 50% farther before stopping than cart A, which has the larger total work done on it?**
>
> *Answer.* Neither. The carts have the same mass, the same initial speed, and the same final speed (0m/s), so they have the same change in kinetic energy, and the same total work done on them. Cart B rolls farther because the applied force stopping it must be smaller, so its kinetic energy is lost more slowly than cart A's.

Sometimes it is hard to identify the force or forces actually doing work on an object:

> **A 500g superball is thrown at 2m/s against a brick wall, where it rebounds with the same speed. At one instant while it is touching the wall, the ball is at rest. How much work is done on the ball to bring it to rest, and what force or forces do the work?**
>
> *Answer.* The initial kinetic energy of the ball is $E_K = \frac{1}{2}mv^2 = \frac{1}{2}(0.5\text{kg})(2\text{m/s})^2 = 1\text{J}$. When the ball is at rest against the wall, the kinetic energy is zero, so the change is -1J. This is the total work done on the ball. The external forces on the ball while it is slowing down are a gravitational force exerted by the earth, a normal force exerted by the wall, and perhaps a static friction force exerted by the wall. Because the ball deforms as a result of hitting the wall, the internal forces that normally keep the ball round become important. Assuming the ball is moving horizontally when it hits, gravitation does no work. Assuming the wall does not move, the normal and static friction forces do no work either. The work done on the ball is done purely by internal (spring-like) forces when the ball deforms.

Momentum and kinetic energy both depend on the mass and the velocity of an object, but they are very different quantities, as shown in this example.

Two blocks are pulled along frictionless surfaces with the same force as shown. Block *m* is pulled until its speed is 2*v*, and block 3*m* is pulled until its speed is *v*. Which block has more work done on it? Which block has the larger impulse delivered to it by the rope?

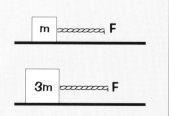

> ***Answer.*** The change in kinetic energy of the small block is $\frac{1}{2}m(2v)^2 = 2mv^2$, so the work done on it by the tension force is $2mv^2$. The change in kinetic energy of the large block is $\frac{1}{2}(3m)v^2 = \frac{3}{2}mv^2$, so the work done on it is $\frac{3}{2}mv^2$, which is smaller than the work done on the small block.
>
> The change in momentum of the small block is $2mv$, and the change in momentum of the large block is $3mv$, so the impulse delivered to the large block is larger than the impulse delivered to the small block.
>
> The small block has more work done on it, but the large block experiences the larger impulse. The force is applied to the small block for a longer distance, but for a shorter time interval. This can happen because the masses of the two blocks are different.

A force can deliver an impulse without doing any work, as shown in these examples.

A toy car is traveling to the right with speed *v* as shown. How much work is needed to reverse the direction of the car? Is there an impulse delivered to the car?

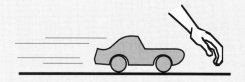

> ***Answer.*** If the final speed of the car is the same as the initial speed, then the change in kinetic energy is zero, and the work done on the car is zero also. However, the car does experience a change in velocity, so there is a change in momentum, and therefore, there must be an impulse delivered to the car. This makes sense because the applied force is to the left during the entire time period.

Also, imagine a basketball bouncing on the floor. The floor exerts a normal force while the ball is touching it. The force points up during the whole time the ball is touching it, so the floor delivers an impulse to the ball and changes its momentum. However, the floor does not move, so the force is exerted through zero displacement, and the work done by the normal force is zero. (Any energy lost during the bounce is caused by forces within the ball.)

Analyzing situations using Conservation of Energy. The law of Conservation of Energy, as it has been presented, applies to the universe as a whole: The total amount of energy remains constant, and cannot change. What <u>can</u> change is how much of it is distributed in (macroscopic) kinetic energy, (macroscopic) potential energy, and microscopic (kinetic and potential) energy. As stated, this law is not particularly convenient or useful for analyzing situations, because we can never describe what is happening in the entire universe.

To analyze specific situations, it is necessary to define a *system*. Unlike the total energy in the universe (a very large, closed system), which cannot change, the total energy of a typical system can change, but only if work is done on the system by external forces. Therefore, to apply energy conservation to a particular system, we use the *Work–Energy Theorem*.

$$W_{\text{external}} = \Delta E_{\text{system}}$$ **Work–Energy Theorem for a system of objects**

where: W_{external} = total work done by <u>external</u> forces on a chosen system

ΔE_{system} = change in the <u>total</u> energy of the system

Let's look at a block bouncing up and down on a spring. At the instant shown, the block is moving upward between its lowest position and its equilibrium position. This means the net force on the block points upward, so it is speeding up. It also means that the spring is stretched from its relaxed state, but getting shorter. Let's look at how the description of this situation changes depending on what we choose as our system. We will consider three different systems: (1) the block itself, (2) the block and spring, and (3) the block, the spring, and the earth (including the air).

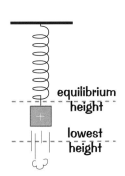

equilibrium height

lowest height

The block itself. When considering the block all by itself, the external forces are a gravitational force, a spring force, and a force of air resistance. Gravitation is doing negative work, and the spring is doing positive work. There is no potential energy in the system, because gravitation and the spring force are <u>outside</u> the system; they are external forces. The kinetic energy of the block is increasing, so the total energy is increasing. We cannot calculate the work done by air resistance, therefore we cannot determine the change in microscopic energy.

The block and spring. When the spring is included in the system, the system has spring potential energy. The external forces are a gravitational force, a force exerted on the spring by the ceiling, and an air resistance force. The external force on the spring exerted by the ceiling does <u>no work</u> on the system, because the ceiling does not move. Because the only external force doing work is gravitation, the total work done on the system is negative, so the total energy of the system is decreasing. The spring potential energy is decreasing, and the kinetic energy of the block and spring is increasing. As before, we cannot determine the change in microscopic energy.

Block, spring, and earth (including air). Neglecting the gravitational forces exerted by the moon, the sun, and other celestial objects, now there are <u>no external</u> forces on the system, and therefore, no work is done by external forces. As in system 2, the spring potential energy is decreasing. When the earth is included, there is gravitational potential energy in the system, which is <u>increasing</u> as the block rises. Because the air is now being included, there are changes in the microscopic energy of the system, as the block disturbs the air surrounding it. Because there is no work done by external forces, the total energy of the system remains constant at all times. The total potential energy is decreasing, because kinetic energy is increasing.

The following table summarizes these ideas.

	SYSTEM BEING CONSIDERED		
FEATURE OF SYSTEM	(1) block alone	(2) block & spring	(3) block, spring, earth (and air)
<u>External</u> forces on system	• gravitation, down, exerted by the earth • spring, up, exerted by the spring • air resistance, down, exerted by the air	• gravitation, down, exerted by the earth • applied, up, exerted by the ceiling on the spring • air resistance, down, exerted by the air	• [none]
<u>Sign</u> of the work done by each external force	• negative work done by gravitation • positive work done by the spring force • [cannot determine work done by air resistance]	• negative work done by gravitation • <u>no</u> work done by the applied force on spring • [cannot determine work done by air resistance]	• [NA]
<u>Changes</u> in:			
Kinetic Energy	• E_K increasing	• E_K increasing	• E_K increasing
Gravitational Potential Energy	• [no U_g in system, because F_g external]	• [no U_g in system, because F_g external]	• U_g increasing
Spring Potential Energy	• [no U_s in system, because F_s external]	• U_s decreasing	• U_s decreasing
Microscopic Energy	• change in E_{micro} unknown	• change in E_{micro} unknown	• E_{micro} increasing
Total Energy of the System	• E_{system} increasing	• E_{system} decreasing	• [no change, because no external forces]

Note these features of this table:

- When a gravitational or spring force is external to a system, its effect should be considered part of $W_{external}$ rather than ΔU. Only when the earth is part of a system should U_g be used, and only when the spring is part of a system should U_s be used. It is usually easier to use potential energy rather than calculate the work, so we often choose our systems to include the earth and all springs in the situation.

- Work is done by an external force only when the force is exerted through a non-zero displacement. In system 1 (block only) the spring force is exerted on the block, which is moving, so the work is non-zero. In system 2 (block & spring), an applied force is exerted by the ceiling, which does not move, so the work is zero.

Often we need to use kinematics and dynamics to analyze a situation before we can use conservation of energy to make a comparison.

A ball is shot out of a spring-loaded cannon and follows trajectory A, reaching a maximum height h. Later, the same ball is shot and it follows trajectory B with the same maximum height. In which case does the system have more energy?

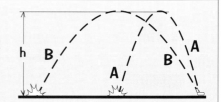

Answer. Let's ignore air resistance, and define the system to be the earth, the spring (in the cannon) and the ball. In each case, no work is done by external forces, so the energy is same at every point along each trajectory. At height h, the gravitational potential energies of the two balls are the same. In which case is the <u>kinetic</u> energy larger, or are they the same? Because the ball reaches the same maximum height in each case, the vertical component of its initial velocity must also be the same, and it takes the same amount of time to reach height h. But trajectory B is longer, so the horizontal component of the ball's velocity (which is constant throughout) must be larger in case B than in case A. Therefore, at the top of trajectory B, the ball is going faster, and has more kinetic energy, than at the top of trajectory A. There is more energy in case B than in case A.

Conservation of Energy can be used to determine where energy goes during a collision.

A 1kg cart traveling at 80cm/s collides <u>and</u> <u>sticks</u> to a 1.5kg cart at rest. How much energy is lost in this collision? How is energy redistributed?

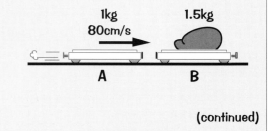

(continued)

(continued)

Answer. We choose the system to be the two carts. The external forces on the system are two gravitational forces exerted by the earth (one on each cart), and two vertical normal forces exerted by the surface. The horizontal contact force exerted by each cart on the other is internal to the system. The displacements of the carts are horizontal, so the gravitational forces and the vertical normal forces do no work. Therefore the change in total energy of the system is zero. <u>No energy is lost</u>.

The final speed of the pair is found from momentum conservation to be 32cm/s. The change in kinetic energy of the system is –0.141J, and there is no change in its potential energy. Some of the kinetic energy of the carts has been converted to microscopic energy by the forces that the two carts exert on each other. The change in microscopic energy is 0.141J.

Conservation of Energy can also be used to derive the change in microscopic energy due to friction. When a box is pulled at constant speed as shown, the work done by the (constant) force F is FD. This is the amount of energy deposited into the molecules

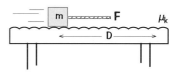

of the two surfaces touching each other. The energy is <u>shared</u> by the two surfaces, and we do not know how much each gets, but we know that the <u>total</u> change in microscopic energy is FD. In terms of the coefficient of friction and the normal force, the relationship is:

$$\Delta E_{\text{micro}} = \mu_k F_N D \qquad\qquad \textbf{change in microscopic energy due to friction}$$

where D is the <u>relative</u> displacement of the two surfaces in contact. This expression can be verified in a number of other situations. For example, what if the applied force F in the diagram above is <u>larger</u> than the friction force on the box? The box would speed up, and its macroscopic kinetic energy would increase. However, the amount of energy deposited in the surfaces would be exactly the same. In fact, the <u>same expression</u> (i.e., $\mu_k F_N D$) would result if you were to solve for the change in microscopic energy due to friction in <u>any</u> of the situations shown below.

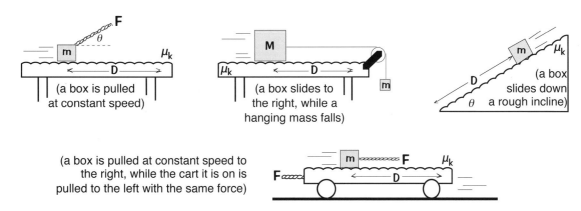

An expression may be derived for air resistance as well. Imagine a ball of mass m falling at terminal velocity. After the ball has fallen a distance D, the work done by gravitation is mgD. This energy has been transferred to microscopic energy due to air resistance. In terms of the force of air resistance, the relationship is:

$$\Delta E_{\mathrm{micro}} = F_{\mathrm{air}}D = Av^2D \qquad \textbf{change in microscopic energy due to air resistance}$$

where A = shape parameter for the object, and v = speed of the object relative to the surrounding air. When the speed is not constant, the same relationship applies, but we must be more careful in applying it, because the force is not constant. We must imagine very small displacements—displacement so small that the speed may be considered constant during it.

3.8   USING ENERGY IDEAS AND PRINCIPLES TO SOLVE PROBLEMS

Now that you can analyze physical situations using energy ideas, you can apply energy ideas properly when solving problems. For example, when solving problems, you often need to choose a system to be considered. This choice usually depends on which forces you would like to consider *external* to the system and which forces you would like to consider *internal*. We start with the Work–Kinetic Energy Theorem.

Solving problems using the Work–Kinetic Energy Theorem. The Work–Kinetic Energy Theorem is written:

$$W_{\mathrm{total}} = \Delta E_K \qquad \textbf{Work–Kinetic Energy Theorem}$$

where: W_{total} = total work done by <u>all</u> forces, external <u>and</u> internal

ΔE_K = <u>change</u> in total kinetic energy, macroscopic <u>and</u> microscopic

In general there are two ways to proceed: (1) Knowing the forces as functions of <u>displacement</u> allows you to calculate the total work done on a system, which you can use to learn something about the masses and speeds of the objects in the system; or (2) knowing the masses and speeds of objects allows you to calculate the change in kinetic energy of the system, which you can use to learn something about the forces exerted on the system. We provide one example of each type.

A 500kg trailer is pulled by a truck. After stopping at a traffic light on a long, straight road, the truck pulls on the trailer with the force shown to the right. What is the speed of the trailer after traveling 50m?

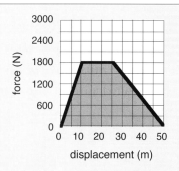

Answer. <u>Analysis</u>. Neglecting air resistance and frictional effects, the only force doing work on the trailer is the applied force. Because the force is not constant, we must use areas to calculate the total work done by it. Then, we can use the Work–Kinetic Energy Theorem to find the change in kinetic energy. We know the mass and initial speed of the trailer, so we can find the final speed of the trailer after going 50m.

<u>Solution</u>. Assuming the applied force is horizontal (and therefore parallel to the displacement), the total work is the area under the force vs. displacement graph, which is the area of a trapezoid:

$$W_{\text{total}} = W_{\text{applied}} = \tfrac{1}{2}(50\text{m} + 15\text{m})(1800\text{N}) = 58{,}500\text{J}.$$

This is the change in kinetic energy of the trailer. Its initial kinetic energy is zero, so its final kinetic energy is 58,500J:

$$E_{K,f} = \tfrac{1}{2}m(v_f)^2 = 58{,}500\text{J}.$$

Using $m = 500$kg and solving for v_f, we get:

$$v_f = \sqrt{\frac{2E_{K,f}}{m}} = \sqrt{\frac{2(58{,}500\text{J})}{500\text{kg}}} = 15.3\text{m/s}$$

The speed of the trailer is about 15m/s (about 34mph) after being pulled 50m.

Above, we applied the Work–Kinetic Energy Theorem and the definition of total work to determine the final speed of the trailer. Below, we apply the Work–Kinetic Energy Theorem and the definition of kinetic energy to determine the maximum force exerted on the trailer.

A 900kg trailer is pulled by a 2000kg truck. After stopping at a traffic light on a long, straight road, the truck pulls on the trailer with a constantly increasing force for 40m, then with a constant force for the next 60m. If the speed of the truck and trailer is 40mph (about 18m/s) at this time, what is the maximum force exerted on the trailer?

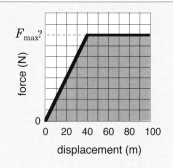

Answer. *Analysis.* We know the initial and final speeds of the trailer, so we can find the change in its kinetic energy. By the Work–Kinetic Energy Theorem, this must be equal to the total work done on the trailer. Neglecting air resistance and frictional effects, the only force doing work on the trailer is the applied force. Because the force is not constant, we again use areas to calculate the total work done by it. The area will depend on the unknown maximum force, so we will be able to solve for it.

    Solution. The initial kinetic energy is zero, so the change in kinetic energy is equal to the final kinetic energy of the trailer:

$$\Delta E_K = E_{K,f} - E_{K,i} = \tfrac{1}{2} m v_f^2 - (0) = \tfrac{1}{2}(900\text{kg})(18\text{m/s})^2 = 146{,}000\text{J}$$

This is the total work done on the trailer. Assuming the applied force is horizontal (and therefore parallel to the displacement), the total work is the area under the force vs. displacement graph, which is the area of a trapezoid:

$$W_{\text{total}} = W_{\text{applied}} = \tfrac{1}{2}(100\text{m} + 60\text{m})(F_{\text{max}}) = (80\text{m})F_{\text{max}} = 146{,}000\text{J}$$

Solving for the maximum force, we get:

$$F_{\text{max}} = \frac{146{,}000\text{J}}{80\text{m}} = 1825\text{N}$$

The maximum force exerted on the trailer by the truck is about 1800N.

Note that these two examples used two very similar situations, but the way in which the Work–Kinetic Energy Theorem was used is very different. As with all the other principles you have learned so far, you must be flexible in how you use the Work–Kinetic Energy Theorem to solve problems. The graphic at the top of the next page shows the relationships between ideas and the strategies used to solve problems with the Work–Kinetic Energy Theorem.

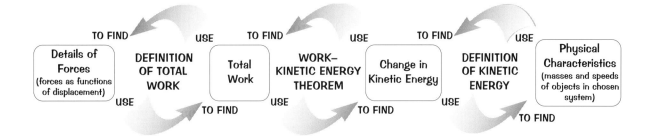

Solving problems using Conservation of Energy. The first step in using Conservation of Energy to solve problems is to choose the system. Usually, it is easier to use potential energy stored in springs and in gravitational interactions than to calculate the work done by springs and by gravitation. Therefore, we usually include all springs and the earth when we choose our system.

Keep in mind that the relationship we are using to apply Conservation of Energy <u>looks like</u> the Work–Kinetic Energy Theorem, but it is different, and the differences are important. The following table summarizes the similarities and differences between the Work–Kinetic Energy Theorem and the Work–Energy Theorem.

	Work–Kinetic Energy Theorem	Work–Energy Theorem
Relationship	$W_{\text{total}} = \Delta E_K$	$W_{\text{external}} = \Delta E_{\text{system}}$
Similarities	• involves a system of objects.	• (same)
	• involves "work" done by forces on the objects in the system.	• (same)
	• involves kinetic energy.	• (same)
	• involves a change in "energy".	• (same)
Differences	• involves the <u>total</u> work done by <u>all</u> forces, both internal and external to the chosen system.	• involves only the work done by <u>external</u> forces exerted on the objects in the chosen system.
	• involves only the change in total <u>kinetic</u> energy of the objects in the system.	• involves the change in <u>total</u> energy of the objects in the system.

Let's start with some examples in which the work done by external forces is zero or negligibly small.

A metal ball is attached to a 1.2m rope and released from rest at an angle of 30° relative to the horizontal. Estimate the speed of the ball at the lowest point in its swing.

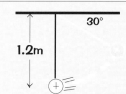

Answer. *Analysis*. Treating the ball and the earth as a system, and ignoring the effects of air resistance, the only external force on the system is a tension force exerted by the rope.

The work done by the tension force is zero, because the force always points perpendicular to the displacement of the ball. Therefore, no work is done by any external forces, and the total energy of the system is constant. The total energy consists of kinetic energy of the ball and gravitational potential energy. We do not know the mass of the ball, but because both the kinetic energy and the potential energy are proportional to the mass, we can solve for the speed of the ball at the bottom of its swing.

Solution. The total work done by external forces is zero, so the change in total energy is zero also. The change in total energy is the sum of the change in kinetic energy, potential energy, and microscopic energy. The change in kinetic energy is $\frac{1}{2}mv_f^2$, and the change in potential energy is $mg\Delta y$. The change in microscopic energy is zero because we are ignoring air resistance. Solving for the final speed, we get the relationship $v_f = \sqrt{-2g\Delta y}$.

$$W_{external} = \Delta E_{system}$$

$$W_{tension} = \Delta E_K + \Delta U + \Delta E_{micro}$$

$$(0) = \left[\tfrac{1}{2}mv_f^2 - 0\right] + \left[mg\Delta y\right] + (0)$$

$$0 = \tfrac{1}{2}mv_f^2 + mg\Delta y$$

$$v_f = \sqrt{-2g\Delta y}$$

$$= \sqrt{-2(10\text{N/kg})(-0.6\text{m})}$$

$$= \sqrt{12\text{m}^2/\text{s}^2} = 3.46\text{m/s}$$

The change in height is negative, and has a magnitude of 0.6m. Using $g = 10\text{N/kg} = 10\text{m/s}^2$, and evaluating the expression derived for v_f, we get about 3.5m/s as the speed of the metal ball when it is at the bottom of its swing.

Note that we do not know the mass of the ball, yet we are able determine its speed at the bottom of its swing. This means that almost <u>any</u> object attached to this string and dropped from an angle of 30° has the same speed at the lowest point in its trajectory, as long as the object is heavy enough to ignore the effects of air resistance.

Here is another example in which the total work done by forces external to the chosen system is negligibly small.

A 400g toy car is pressed up against a spring of spring constant 5N/cm, and released from rest. The relaxed length of the spring is 24cm, and initially it is compressed 4cm. Estimate the speed of the car just as it loses contact with the spring.

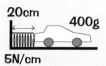

Answer. <u>Analysis</u>. Let's choose the spring and the toy car as the system. The external forces are: a gravitational force exerted by the earth, a force exerted by the wall, a normal force exerted by the floor, a force of air resistance and (perhaps) a friction force exerted by the floor. Because the car moves horizontally, the gravitational force does no work. Because the wall does not move, the force exerted by the wall does no work either. The only forces that do any work are the forces of air resistance and friction. Let's assume that the work done by these forces is small compared to the transfers of energy going on inside the system. This means that energy is constant. In other words, during this process, the change in total energy is zero. There is no gravitational potential energy in the system because the earth is outside the chosen system. The kinetic energy is increasing, while the spring potential energy is decreasing. We assume the microscopic energy stays the same.

<u>Solution</u>. The change in kinetic energy is:

$$\Delta E_K = E_{K,f} - E_{K,i} = \frac{1}{2}mv_f^2 - 0 = \frac{1}{2}mv_f^2.$$

where v_f is the speed of the toy car just as it loses contact with the spring. The change in spring potential energy is:

$$\Delta U_s = U_{s,f} - U_{s,i} = 0 - \frac{1}{2}k(L - L_0)^2 = -\frac{1}{2}k(L - L_0)^2.$$

The change in total energy is zero, so all changes must add to zero:

$$\Delta E_{\text{system}} = 0$$

$$\Delta E_K + \Delta U_s + \Delta E_{\text{micro}} = 0$$

$$\left[\frac{1}{2}mv_f^2\right] + \left[-\frac{1}{2}k(L - L_0)^2\right] + (0) = 0$$

The only unknown in this equation is v_f, so we can solve for it:

$$v_f = \sqrt{\frac{k(L - L_0)^2}{m}} = \sqrt{\frac{500\text{N/m}(0.04\text{m})^2}{0.4\text{kg}}} = \sqrt{2\text{m}^2/\text{s}^2} = 1.41\text{m/s}.$$

Ignoring frictional effects and air resistance, the toy car is moving at about 140cm/s when it loses contact with the spring.

The following example is a situation in which work is done by external forces.

A 600g wooden block is pulled along a rough table as shown, starting from rest. The coefficient of friction is 0.12. If the speed of the block is 40cm/s after it has been pulled for 80cm, what is the applied force on the block?

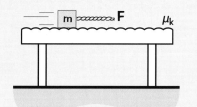

Answer. _Analysis_. We choose the block and the table as the system. The table is included because kinetic friction is present. We are ignoring air resistance. The external forces are a gravitational force on the table, a gravitational force on the block, a normal force on the table (exerted by the floor), a static friction force on the table (also exerted by the floor), and the applied force F. The only external force that does work on this system is the applied force.

Some of the work done by F increases the kinetic energy of the block, and some of it increases the microscopic energy of the block and table. There is no potential energy in the system. We have enough information to find the changes in both microscopic and kinetic energy, so we can solve for the applied force.

Solution. Kinetic friction between the surface and the block causes a change in microscopic energy of the system, which is positive and equal to:

$$\Delta E_{\text{micro}} = \mu_k F_N D = \mu_k mg D$$

where D is the distance traveled by the block. The change in kinetic energy is also positive and equal to:

$$\Delta E_K = \frac{1}{2} m v_f^2 - (0) = \frac{1}{2} m v_f^2$$

There is no potential energy is the chosen system. The change in total energy is equal to sum of the changes above:

$$\Delta E_{\text{system}} = \Delta E_K + \Delta U + \Delta E_{\text{micro}} = \left[\frac{1}{2} m v_f^2 \right] + (0) + (\mu_k mg D)$$

The total work done by external forces is done by the applied force only:

$$W_{\text{external}} = W_F = FD$$

Conservation of Energy means that these two quantities are equal:

$$W_{\text{external}} = \Delta E_{\text{system}} \quad \Rightarrow \quad FD = \frac{1}{2} m v_f^2 + \mu_k mg D$$

The only unknown in the equation on the right is F. Solving for it, we get:

$$F = 0.78\text{N} = \text{applied force on the block}$$

When work is done by external forces, energy is either added to the system (when the work is positive) or taken away from the system (when the work is negative). In fact, the work done is the amount of energy exchanged with the system. Therefore, the total work done is the change in the total energy of the system. This is why the Work–Energy Theorem is so closely related to Conservation of Energy.

This is how we represent the problem-solving strategies derived from Conservation of Energy:

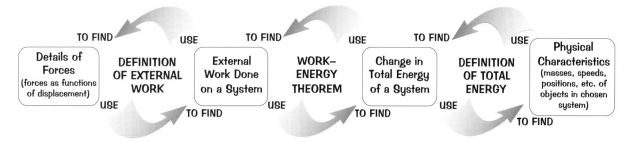

The Work–Energy Theorem is used to apply energy conservation to a particular system. When the total work done by external forces is zero, the total amount of energy in the system is constant, even though the forms of energy within the system may change.

Summary of energy ideas and principles. We now have a number of new "state" quantities involving energy: kinetic energy, E_K; gravitational potential energy, U_g; elastic potential energy, U_s; microscopic energy, E_{micro}; and total energy in a system, E_{system}. They are all scalar quantities, and represent different features of a system. We also have many new "process" quantities. The work W can be used to describe how energy is given to or taken from an object or a system of objects. During a process, any of the state quantities may change as well. For example, when the speed of an object changes, its kinetic energy changes. When the length of a spring changes, its elastic potential energy changes.

We also have a new physical law—Conservation of Energy—and two new problem-solving principles: the Work–Kinetic Energy Theorem and the Work–Energy Theorem. Combined with our knowledge of how forces are exerted on different objects, we are able to use these ideas to analyze many different types of situations and solve lots of problems.

Summary of conservation laws. You have learned two very important and very useful conservation laws—Conservation of Momentum and Conservation of Energy—as well as all the concepts needed to apply them properly, such as impulse, work, kinetic energy, potential energy, and microscopic energy.

One of the reasons we focus so much attention on these new principles is that scientists have never found a situation in which they are not true. In certain cases, when studying a particular system, some of the energy or momentum in the system seemed to disappear. It turned out that a previously undetected particle was taking energy and momentum away. By insisting that these conservation laws were true, new particles were hypothesized and later discovered.

Another reason we use conservation laws is that the application of dynamics is not always practical to understand and predict the behavior of a system. Applying Conservation of Momentum and Energy allows us to analyze situations more easily.

These are not the only conservation laws. There are many more. In general, when analyzing new situations, scientists look for new combinations of physical characteristics that are conserved. For example, in chemical reactions, mass and electric charge are conserved. In nuclear reactions, mass is not conserved, and energy (as we have defined it) seems to be created or destroyed. We find that mass is actually a third "form" of energy, to go with kinetic and potential energy. When we include "mass energy" in the description of the total energy of the system, energy is always conserved.

As we study other areas of physics, such as electricity and magnetism, fluids, thermodynamics, wave phenomena, light, sound, and radioactivity, we will constantly do two things: (1) We will apply the principles you have learned so far to each new situation, and (2) we will look for the new conservation laws that govern the behavior of the objects in each new situation.

In the next chapter, we show you how to put these first three chapters together—how to combine kinematics, dynamics, and conservation laws to analyze any situation and solve many problems in mechanics.

CONCEPT-BASED PROBLEM SOLVING

Introduction. In the 3 previous chapters, you have studied *Motion, Interactions* and *Conservation Laws*. You have already solved a lot of problems within each topic, but we would like you to be able to solve problems without knowing the topic first. To do this, you must organize what you know. Organizing your knowledge will help you to analyze situations using concepts first, before choosing an approach and solving a problem. We call this *concept-based problem solving*.

Consider the following problem:

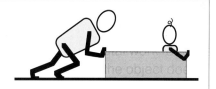

A 40kg boy is playing with his 20kg sister who is sitting in a box on the floor. Starting from rest, he pushes the box with a constant horizontal force of 150N for 2m and then jumps into the box, which stops after sliding 3m more. Estimate the coefficient of friction between the box and the floor.

How should this problem be solved? More importantly, how should you <u>decide</u> how to solve this problem? Should you draw a free-body diagram? If so, is one free-body diagram enough? Should you use a graph? If so, what kind of graph? What concepts are relevant for understanding this situation? What forces are most important, and which (if any) can be neglected? What other assumptions need to be made? Should you use Newton's laws, or momentum ideas, or energy ideas? These are just some of the questions you might ask yourself before attempting to solve the problem. This is a difficult problem, and no equation you have ever seen will allow you to solve for the coefficient of friction using the given information. That is why a conceptual analysis must precede manipulating equations.

First, we will present the physicist's view of mechanics and explain how you can develop your own view; then, we will show how to use your own system to analyze situations and solve problems. You will see that efficient and successful problem solving starts with listing, then prioritizing and interconnecting, all the concepts associated with mechanics and with problem solving. We will come back to the above problem later.

4.1 A PHYSICIST'S VIEW OF MECHANICS

What is meant by a "view of mechanics"? Stated most simply, it means "how ideas in mechanics are organized that permit recall, analysis, and execution when solving problems, explaining phenomena, answering questions, etc." Everyone has a view of mechanics, whether they are fully aware of it or not. The Minds•On Physics activities are designed to make you aware of your own views and the views of other students, so that you can modify your views and help others change their views when they fail to work. Each one of you has a slightly different view, and it is constantly changing as you gain experience in physics. (But your views share features with your classmates' views, which allows us to create meaningful experiences for you!) Every expert in physics also has an individual view or *structure*, and these structures all share some features with each other. An expert's organizational structure is usually created through extensive reflection guided by a few motivational factors, such as:

(1) Which ideas are most useful for analyzing situations, explaining phenomena, answering questions, solving problems, etc.?

(2) Which ideas apply to the greatest number of situations?

(3) How should the ideas be organized so that they can be rapidly recalled and used?

(4) How should the ideas be organized so that they are used properly?

As a result, most experts, no matter what their field happens to be, have created their own organizational scheme which involves first, <u>prioritizing</u> ideas according to generality and usefulness, and second, <u>interconnecting</u> ideas to permit rapid recall and proper application.

Prioritizing ideas in mechanics. What have you learned so far in mechanics? The diagram below shows a partial list of all the ideas introduced and encountered, arranged in the order in which they were presented.

position, origin, origin of a graph, coordinate axes, point of reference,
one-dimensional motion, coordinate system, scale, representations,
magnitude & direction, components, directed line segment, ...,
position vs. time graphs, displacement, ..., velocity, speed,
average velocity, time interval, instantaneous velocity, ...,
slope of position vs. time, ..., area below acceleration vs. time, ...,
dynamics, interactions, forces, ..., newtons, contact forces,
action-at-a-distance forces, ..., empirical force laws, fundamental force laws, ...,
free-body diagrams,net force, Newton's laws of motion, mass, weight, ...,
equilibrium, ..., ..., conservation laws, system, impulse, momentum,
impulse–momentum theorem, conservation of momentum, ..., work, joules,
kinetic energy, work–energy theorem, ..., conservation of energy,
potential energy, microscopic energy, macroscopic energy, ...

Any list necessarily skips and leaves out ideas that are considered not important. Listed in chronological order, there is no indication of which ideas are more important than others. We must prioritize these ideas if we are to have any chance of ever using them successfully.

The most widely useful ideas in the parts of mechanics we have studied so far are Newton's Laws, The Impulse–Momentum Theorem, Conservation of Momentum, the Work–Energy Theorem, and Conservation of Energy. They are called *physical principles*, and many problems are solved by applying one or more of them. These are the most important ideas in physics, because they can be used to solve a wide range of problems.

Each physical principle involves many *concepts*. For example, Newton's second law relates the concept of *net force* exerted on an object to the concepts of *mass* and *acceleration*. Conservation of Energy relates the *total work* done on a *system* by *external forces* to the *change* in the *total energy* of the *system*. Because concepts are essential for understanding and discussing physical principles, they are the next most important ideas in physics.

Next in our prioritization scheme are *equations*, of which there are many types: *physical laws, definitions, empirical laws,* and *derived relations*. Equations are the mathematical representations of how different ideas are related to each other. They are needed to actually solve a problem for the desired unknown.

The most important type of equation is the *physical law*. Put simply, it is the mathematical form of a physical principle. Efficient and successful problem solving often begins with choosing a physical principle, so we often begin a solution by writing down a physical law.

To properly apply a physical law, you must know what it means and how to write it in terms of other ideas. This inevitably requires that you know *definitions*. For instance, in a problem, you are seldom given the net force exerted on an object or its acceleration. More commonly, you are given its mass, some kinematic information (such as how far it moves in a certain period of time), and some physical characteristics of the situation. In order to apply Newton's second law, you must eventually apply the definitions of net force and acceleration.

Often, the definition of one concept involves the definition of another. For example, the *total energy* is defined to be the sum of the *total kinetic energy*, the *total potential energy*, and the *total mass energy*, and the *total microscopic energy*. The *total kinetic energy* is the sum of the *kinetic energies* of each of the individual objects in the system. The *kinetic energy* of a single object is one-half its *mass* times the square of its *speed*. We can go on and on, expanding each concept in terms of its definition using more basic concepts. At every level, definitions are essential for solving physics problems. Definitions are always valid, whether or not they are needed for or relevant to a particular situation.

Some definitions, such as the net force and the work done by particular forces, use *empirical force laws*. Empirical laws are not always true, but they are valid for a wide enough range of physical conditions and characteristics that they are extremely useful for understanding many situations. For example, the weight of an object of mass m is equal to mg only near the surface of the earth. If we go deep inside the earth, or far above the earth, we must use a different relationship.

The least useful type of equation is a *derived relation*. As its name implies, it is an equation that is derived for a certain set of assumptions and conditions, which must be recalled along with the equation in order to properly apply it to a new situation. For example, in chapter 1 (Motion), we derived a kinematic equation relating the position of an object at a particular time to its initial position, initial velocity, and acceleration, <u>assuming the acceleration was constant</u>.

$$x(t) = x_0 + v_{0x}t + \frac{1}{2}a_x t^2$$

If the acceleration is not constant, or if the initial position and velocity are not known, then we cannot use this equation. The main drawback with derived relations is that many people apply them without considering whether or not the given situation matches the conditions used to derive them.

The priority scheme we have just presented is shown below and on the next page, along with some examples.

PHYSICAL PRINCIPLES	Newton's 2nd law Newton's 3rd law	Cons. of Momentum Impulse–Momentum Thm.	Cons. of Energy Work–Kin. Energy Thm.
CONCEPTS	net force, mass, acceleration, free-body diagram, velocity, change in velocity, time, position, change in position, displacement, tension force, normal force, spring force, gravitational force, kinetic friction force, static friction force, etc.	impulse, momentum, system, net impulse, total momentum, change in momentum, change in total momentum	work, kinetic energy, total work, change in kinetic energy, speed, total energy, potential energy, total work done by external forces, gravitational potential energy, spring potential energy, work done by tension force, work done by normal force, etc.
EQUATIONS			
PHYSICAL LAWS	$\mathbf{F}_{net} = m\mathbf{a}$ $\mathbf{F}_{\text{on 1 by 2}} = -\mathbf{F}_{\text{on 2 by 1}}$	$\Delta\mathbf{P}_{system} = 0$ $\mathbf{J}_{net} = \Delta\mathbf{P}_{system}$	$W_{external} = \Delta E_{system}$ $W_{total} = \Delta E_K$

(continued on the next page)

PHYSICAL PRINCIPLES	Newton's 2nd law Newton's 3rd law	Cons. of Momentum Impulse–Momentum Thm.	Cons. of Energy Work–Kin. Energy Thm.
EQUATIONS (continued)			
DEFINITIONS	$\mathbf{F}_{net} \equiv \mathbf{F}_1 + \mathbf{F}_2 + \ldots$ $\mathbf{a} \equiv \dfrac{\Delta \mathbf{v}}{\Delta t}$ (Δt small) $\mathbf{v} \equiv \dfrac{\Delta \mathbf{x}}{\Delta t}$ (Δt small) $\Delta \mathbf{v} \equiv \mathbf{v}_2 - \mathbf{v}_1$	$\mathbf{J} \equiv \mathbf{F}\Delta t$ (Δt small) $\mathbf{P}_{system} \equiv \mathbf{p}_1 + \mathbf{p}_2 + \ldots$ $\mathbf{p} \equiv m\mathbf{v}$ $\mathbf{J}_{net} \equiv \mathbf{F}_{net}\Delta t$ (Δt small)	$W_F \equiv F_{\parallel}d$ $W_F \equiv Fd_{\parallel}$ $E_{system} \equiv E_K + U + E_{micro}$ $U \equiv U_g + U_s$ $E_K \equiv \frac{1}{2}mv^2$
EMPIRICAL LAWS	$F_g = mg$ $F_s = kx$ $F_{fk} = \mu_k F_N$ $F_{fs} \leq \mu_s F_N$		$U_g = mgy$ $U_s = \frac{1}{2}kd^2 = \frac{1}{2}k(L - L_0)^2$ $\Delta E_{micro} = \begin{cases} \mu_k F_N D \ \left(\begin{array}{l}\text{sliding}\\\text{friction}\end{array}\right) \\ Av^2 D \ \left(\begin{array}{l}\text{air}\\\text{resistance}\end{array}\right) \end{cases}$
DERIVED RELATIONS	$a = \dfrac{F_{applied}}{m}$	$v_f = \dfrac{mv_0}{m + M}$	$v = \sqrt{2gh}$

There remain some important ideas missing from this priority scheme. For example, there are *mathematical principles*, such as *the area below velocity vs. time is the displacement* and *the slope of velocity vs. time is the acceleration*. Although these are derived using the definitions of certain concepts, they are usually easier to apply than derived relations and are more general than many derived relations. This makes them very useful for analyzing situations and solving problems.

There are more ideas still. For instance, where would you put the ideas of *how to draw a free-body diagram* or *the conditions under which to consider energy ideas*? These ideas require special categories. The first is an example of an *operation*. The second is an example of a *problem-solving ideas*. More examples are shown in the table on the next page.

MATHEMATICAL PRINCIPLES	• the slope of position vs. time is the velocity • the area below velocity vs. time is the displacement • the slope of velocity vs. time is the acceleration • the area below acceleration vs. time is the change in velocity • the area below force vs. time is the impulse delivered by the force • the area below force (parallel to the displacement) vs. displacement is the work done by the force
OPERATIONS AND PROCEDURES	• how to draw a free-body diagram • how to find components of a vector • how to draw a graph of position (or velocity or acceleration or force) vs. time (or displacement) • how to find the direction of a force • how to identify external vs. internal forces • how to compute the area below a graph • how to recognize when there is a change in microscopic energy (etc.)
PROBLEM-SOLVING IDEAS	• Choose the orientation of coordinate axes so that the net force and the acceleration lie along one of the axes. • Draw a free-body diagram to help identify forces, keep track of their directions, and find their components. • Sketch velocity vs. time to relate the displacement of something to its acceleration. • Consider momentum ideas when doing collisions and explosions. • Consider momentum or energy ideas when the forces are not known as functions of time. • Consider energy ideas when the forces are known for a specific displacement. (etc.)

Interconnecting ideas in mechanics. As you can see, the description of the categories used to organize and prioritize ideas in physics involves concepts. Every example, every sentence, seemingly every other word, requires concepts. They are unavoidable. For this reason, we strongly recommend concepts as the basis for relating and interconnecting ideas in mechanics. This is why we call this approach *concept-based problem solving*.

There is an even wider appeal for concepts, however. The big ideas—motion, interactions, forces, momentum, and energy—have been extremely useful for understanding all aspects of the physical world. Many of these ideas are also useful for many fields involving science and technology, such as medicine, biochemistry, and engineering. Also, it is a conceptual understanding of physical systems that can help people analyze day-to-day situations, such as how to drive a car safely based on traffic and weather conditions. In the next section, we describe this method for solving problems.

4.2   CONCEPT-BASED PROBLEM SOLVING

How to <u>start</u> solving a problem. Let's return to the problem posed on the first page of this chapter.

A 40kg boy is playing with his 20kg sister who is sitting in a box on the floor. Starting from rest, he pushes the box with a constant horizontal force of 150N for 2m and then jumps into the box, which stops after sliding 3m more. Estimate the coefficient of friction between the box and the floor.

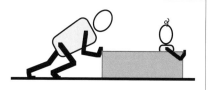

How are we going to solve this problem? Using our priority scheme as a guide, there are typically 3 steps that need to be followed in order to solve a problem.

Step 1. Sort the principles into those that <u>can</u> be used to solve the problem and those that <u>cannot</u>.

Physical principles are at the top of our priority scheme, and efficient problem solving is accomplished when you <u>choose</u> which principle you think is best for the particular problem you are solving. Therefore, you must determine which principles are possible. This step requires a conceptual analysis, because we must understand the situation in order to determine which principles apply and which do not. For this sample problem, we cannot use Conservation of Momentum, because external forces deliver a net impulse to system. Also, we cannot use the Work–Kinetic Energy Theorem, because we do not know how to calculate the work done by friction. We <u>might</u> be able to use Conservation of Energy, but we must be careful about how we choose our system, because we are not given any information about how much microscopic energy (i.e., stored energy in his body) is converted by the boy into macroscopic energy (e.g., kinetic energy of himself, the box, and the sister). So, we are left with Newton's laws, the Impulse–Momentum Theorem, and Conservation of Energy.

Step 2. Choose one of the valid principles.

This step usually involves looking at the situation again. For example, although Newton's second law and the Impulse–Momentum Theorem are valid, there is no given information about the time intervals. Rather there is information about forces, masses, and displacements. This suggests energy ideas. The only unknown in the problem is the desired unknown, the coefficient of kinetic friction. So we choose the law of Conservation of Energy.

Step 3. Apply the chosen principle and try to solve for the desired unknown.

This step often requires a set of common procedures, such as:

(a) Choose the time intervals over which the chosen principle will be applied.
(b) Choose the system to be considered during each time interval.
(c) Apply definitions, empirical laws, mathematical principles and/or derived relations until the original equation is written in terms of known quantities.
(d) Make assumptions needed to simplify the problem.
(e) Recognize constraints on the situation.
(f) Solve the resulting equation(s) for the desired unknown.

You have already done all these procedures many times, even if you are not aware of it. Some of them you do automatically, such as choosing a system or choosing the time interval.

In our example, there are two time intervals that need to be considered separately—during the first 2m and during the last 3m of the motion. The boy has an unknown static friction force on him, so for the first 2m we consider only the sister, the box, and the floor. The external forces are gravitation, the force applied by the brother, and forces that keep the floor stationary. (The normal and friction forces exerted by the floor on the box are internal forces.) Positive work is done by the brother, no work is done by gravitation, and no work is done by the forces keeping the floor at rest. The total work causes a change in the speed of the sister-box system, but some of this energy goes into microscopic energy due to friction. In fact, after 2 meters the speed is maximum. Conservation of Energy yields one equation relating the coefficient of friction (μ_k) to the maximum speed (v_{max}). We do not know the speed of the brother as he jumps into the box, but we will assume that it is v_{max}. Afterwards, there are <u>no</u> forces doing work (on the boy-floor-box-sister system). The kinetic energy of the boy, box, and sister is converted entirely into microscopic energy due to friction. Applying Conservation of Energy again, we get another relationship between μ_k and v_{max}. Therefore we can solve for μ_k. Two free-body diagrams will help keep track of all the forces and their directions. The mathematical solution is shown below.

During the first 2 meters:

The system is the floor, the sister and the box. In order to find the change in microscopic energy, we need to know the normal force exerted by the floor and the relative displacement between the floor and the box. Neglecting the mass of the box, the normal force is equal to the weight of the sister, mg, and the relative displacement is $d_1 = 2m$. Applying Conservation of Energy:

$$W_{external} = \Delta E_{system}$$

$$F_{applied}\, d_1 = \Delta E_K + \Delta E_{micro}$$

$$F_{applied}\, d_1 = \tfrac{1}{2} m v_{max}^2 + \mu_k mg d_1 \qquad [1]$$

where $F_{applied} = 150N$, $d_1 = 2m$, and $m = 20kg$ = mass of the <u>sister</u>. Note that there are two unknowns in the third equation, μ_k and v_{max}.

During the last 3m:

The system is now the floor, <u>both</u> children, and the box. Applying Conservation of Energy again:

$$W_{external} = \Delta E_{system}$$

$$0 = \Delta E_K + \Delta E_{micro}$$

$$0 = -\tfrac{1}{2}(M + m)v_{max}^2 + \mu_k(M + m)gd_2$$

Solving for v_{max}^2 in this equation and inserting the result into equation [1] above, we get:

$$F_{applied}\, d_1 = \mu_k mg d_2 + \mu_k mg d_1$$

Solving for μ_k and evaluating, we get:

$$\mu_k = \frac{F_{applied}}{mg} \times \frac{d_1}{d_1 + d_2} = \frac{150N}{200N} \times \frac{2m}{5m} = 0.3$$

The coefficient of kinetic friction between the box and the floor is about 0.3. Note that the result does not depend on the mass of the boy.

How to <u>finish</u> solving a problem. In the description above, we showed how a problem might be approached using concepts first and equations last. It was only an approach, and no options were given if the first approach failed. Unfortunately most problems are not solved as straightforwardly as that one. What should you do when you are stuck? What if there are more unknowns in the problem than there are equations? How should you check your answer to make sure that it makes sense? These are all important questions that often arise when solving real problems. In the remainder of this chapter we provide some hints to help you solve all sorts of problems.

Create sketches and diagrams.

If you become stuck or confused when you are trying to apply your chosen principle, it is often a good idea to make yourself some drawings of the situation. For example, consider the diagram at right. The drawing contains all given information except the force exerted by the boy on the box, and it shows when different events occur. Sketches of velocity vs. time are also excellent for representing the motion of the objects in the situation.

Count the number of equations and the number of unknowns.

When you have simplified your equations as much as possible and re-written them using as many given quantities as you can, count the number of unknowns in each equation. If the number of "independent" equations is equal to the number of unknowns in them, then you can always solve for the desired unknown. (If two equations are combined to form a third equation, the third equation is not "independent" of the other two.) If you have fewer equations than unknowns, then you must find more equations. Sometimes the missing equation is a definition, empirical law, mathematical principle, or derived relation, so consider those types of relations first. If that fails, there might be a constraint missing. For example, when two objects are connected by a string passing over a pulley, the magnitudes of their accelerations are equal. When no other equations can be found, what's missing is probably another physical principle.

Challenge your assumptions.

Each of us, expert or not, often makes assumptions regarding a situation without realizing it. These assumptions can severely hinder the problem-solving process because we are not aware of its implications. For instance, in the sample problem, we might have assumed that we could determine the work done by all forces and decided that the Work–Kinetic Energy Theorem would be the best principle to apply. At some point, we would become stuck. The way to become unstuck is to realize that the conditions needed to apply the Work–Kinetic Energy Theorem are not present. One of the quantities—the work done by sliding friction—is unknown and impossible to determine. The only way to get unstuck is to become aware of any assumptions that were made and challenge them.

In general it is a good idea to cycle through the problem-solving steps looking for alternative ways of approaching the problem. For example, you can return to step 1 at any time and check to make sure you have sorted the principles properly. Or you can go back to step 2 and try a different principle and see if you are more successful applying that one.

Check your answer.

You cannot really be sure your solution is correct until you have checked your answer. Some students check their algebra, but that is not really enough, because even if the algebra is correct there could be mistakes in the physics. Also, even if there is a mistake in the algebra, it is unlikely that you will find it by reviewing what you have done.

There are many ways to check your answer. One way is to decide if the answer makes sense given the situation. For instance, if the coefficient of friction was determined to be 3.0, then we would know that there is a mistake somewhere. In particular, knowing that coefficients of friction are usually less than 1.0, we would look for a factor of 5 or 10 that is missing.

Another way to check your answer is by considering limiting or special cases. For example, if you doubled the applied force, how would the answer change? Does this change make sense?

A third way to check your answer is to compute some of the other unknown quantities, and to check for consistency. For example, using a value of 0.3 for μ_k, we can determine that the friction force on the box during the first half of the motion is 60N. After 2m, the change in microscopic energy is 120J. The work done by the boy is 300J, and 120J of that energy goes into microscopic energy, so the sister's kinetic energy must be 180J. The boy weighs twice as much as she does, so his kinetic energy must be 360J, making the total kinetic energy equal to 540J. This is the amount of energy that must be dissipated by friction. After he jumps into the box, the new friction force is 180N, so it would take 3m for the box to stop, as given.

A fourth way to check an answer is to apply a different principle to the situation to see if the numbers make sense. For example, try Newton's 2nd law. The net force on the box and sister is 90N, so their acceleration is 4.5m/s^2 to the right. Using kinematics, we find that to cover 2m would take only about 0.94s, and the maximum speed would be about 4.2m/s. After the boy jumps into the box, the net force is 180N to the left, and so the acceleration is $3m/s^2$ to the left. Therefore it would take about 1.4s for them to stop, and the distance covered is about 3m, again, as given.

Conclusion. Concept-based problem solving is a powerful approach to thinking about the physical world and understanding it. We strongly recommend this approach because it is usually more likely to be successful than other approaches.

The diagram below summarizes the main features of the approach. We can think of solving a problem as traveling through a maze. The three steps described earlier are shown along with a fourth step called "Check your Answer". Central to the figure is "EVALUATE", because at each step you should check to make sure what you have done so far makes sense. Its location in the maze allows you to return to any of the previous steps if necessary. For instance, you might decide that your sort during step 1 was done incorrectly, or you may want to go back to step 2 and choose a different principle.

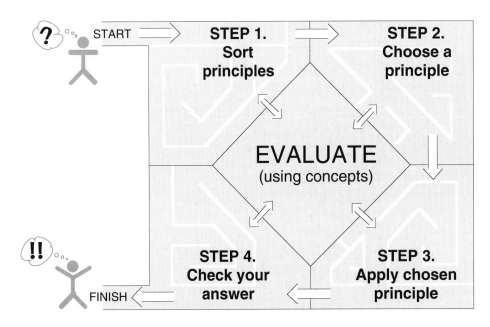

The key to the approach, however, is that concepts are prioritized according to how useful and widely applicable they are for solving problems and for understanding physical situations. Based on our priority scheme we focus on "principles" as being the best starting point of most problems. These ideas will continue to be useful as we study other topics, such as fluids, electricity, magnetism, radioactivity, and nuclear power.